PRAISE FOR JUDY ANDRY'S
A Touching Good-Bye

"I cannot say enough good things about *A Touching Good-Bye*. It should offer great help and consolation to anyone faced with the loss of a loved one. Just being able to help a loved one at this critical time with a loving touch should do much to allay the feeling of helplessness — while knowing at the same time you are offering great comfort. It is in the best tradition of Jin Shin Jyutsu."

Philomena Dooley, R.N.
Jin Shin Jyutsu Instructor

෴෴෴

"After 40 years of medical practice, I welcome thoughtful and interesting treatment modalities that offer comfort, encouragement and hope for people with chronic and terminal illnesses. Judy Andry's knowledge and insight is well illustrated through the stories and the Jin Shin Jyutsu instructions that unfold in this enlightened book."

W. John O'Shaughnessey, M.D.
Past President
Georgia Society of Internal Medicine

෴෴෴

D1554800

"Judy's work with those who are preparing to transition out of the body and the stories she has collected are inspirational and deeply touching. With the tools that are shown in this book, we can assist others in having a peaceful, conscious exit. My gratitude goes to Judy for sharing this with the world."

Jed Schwartz
Jin Shin Jyutsu Instructor

〜〜〜

"I have experienced Jin Shin Jyutsu and have observed its effects on myself and on others. Though I am unable to explain it scientifically, there is no doubt it is effective. I see it as a method of extending love and compassion nonverbally. A 'connection' is experienced at a very deep level in the subconscious mind where, in spite of the apparent condition or outward circumstance, a remembering occurs that brings assurance that ALL IS WELL. Both the giver and the receiver are healed and empowered to move forward without fear."

Jasper B. Becker, M.D.
Author, Divine Health

〜〜〜

A Touching Good-Bye
The Gentle Use of Jin Shin Jyutsu® Acupressure
At Times of Critical Illness and Death

JUDITH B. ANDRY, M.Ed.

AMP&RSAND, INC.

Chicago, Illinois

Where requested, names in the stories have been changed.

Jin Shin Jyutsu® is a registered name and trademark of Jin Shin Jyutsu, Inc. The full name is Jin Shin Jyutsu® Physio-Philosophy.

A Touching Good-Bye is authorized by Jin Shin Jyutsu, Inc.

Disclosure
The Jin Shin Jyutsu information provided in this book is intended to complement, not replace, the advice of your own physician or other healthcare professional whom you should always consult about your individual needs and any symptoms that may require diagnosis or medical attention, and before starting or stopping any medication, or beginning any course of treatment, exercise regimen, or diet. Jin Shin Jyutsu is not intended as a substitute for traditional medical care or emergency intervention.

ISBN 978-0-9818126-0-1

Design: David Robson, Robson Design
Photography: Donald Bradburn, M.D.

Published by
Ampersand, Inc.
1050 North State Street
Chicago, IL 60610

DEDICATION

In loving memory of Mary Burmeister
Founder of Jin Shin Jyutsu in the West

Acknowledgments

My heartfelt thanks to those who shared their stories: Mitzie Adams, Brooke Andry, Ann Bardwell, Susan Brooks, Cynthia Broshi, David Burmeister, Kristen Burnham, Al Canner, Doyle Darraugh, Carlos Gutterres, Betsie Haar, Alicia Heard, Jill Holden, Betsy Matteson, Lisa and Billy Messersmith, Joni Newcomer, Janet Oliver, Jeannette Pasqua, Waltraud Riegger-Krause, Susan Schwartz, Deb Sherman, Bill Thames and Connie White.

To the Jin Shin Jyutsu instructors who so generously share their wisdom and expertise: Susan Brooks, Cynthia Broshi, Muriel Carlton, Philomena Dooley, Petra Elmendorff, Carlos Gutterres, Wayne Hackett, Sara Harper, Ian Harris, Mona Harris, Jill Holden, Iole Lebensztajn, Nathalie Max, Birgitta Meinhardt, Aino Meinhardt, Janet Oliver, Lynne Pflueger, Waltraud Riegger-Krause, Matthias Roth, Jed Schwartz, Susan Schwartz, Margareth Serra, Anita Willoughby.

At the Jin Shin Jyutsu home office in Scottsdale, AZ, David Burmeister, Karen Moore and Jody Friday were always gracious and patient with my questions and requests.

My sanity and the manuscript were saved by emergency computer consultation and direction from Tac, Tippins and Billy Crosby, and Jeff Colon.

For proof reading, advice, and encouragement I thank Mary Jane Phelan, Jackeen Churchill, Donna Newton, Doyle Darraugh, Alicia Heard, Gordon Magonet, M.D., Rose Murray, Barbara Wasser, and Tony Martin.

This book could not have been completed without the good will and editing advice of Betsie Haar, Susan Brooks, and Michael Winninger (Hakuzan Dai-e) who spent an inordinate amount of time reading and re-reading the text in minute detail. I am beyond grateful to them.

My thanks to our friend Donald Bradburn, who graciously gave his time and expertise taking photographs in our patio of models Mary Jane Phelan, Suzie Isaacs, and me.

I thank my editor and publisher, Suzie Isaacs, for recognizing the potential of this book, figuring out a way to open my old "floppy discs," and encouraging me to continue with this project that had been "lost" to the elements and computer failure.

And I thank my husband, Allain Andry, renowned author of *Louie the Buoy: A Hurricane Story*, for his love, patience, and good cheer, and most of all, for the title of this book: *A Touching Good-Bye*.

Contents

Introduction

Along with my job as Elementary School Counselor at the Academy of the Sacred Heart in New Orleans, I maintained a private counseling practice, including workshops on using Reality Therapy in everyday life, and wrote and gave public lectures on Parenting Adolescents. This was already a full schedule in 1983, and then our only daughter became engaged. All of these were positive, fulfilling and, in the case of planning the wedding, very happy endeavors. So why did I have such aches in my neck and shoulders? Why did all of my joints ache? Why was I having so many headaches?

When our friend, Charles, called after getting the wedding invitation, I asked him how I could get in touch with the people he had talked about in Scottsdale, Arizona. He had tried to tell me for several years about the acupressure work he had been studying there. His answer: "I'll be there in ten minutes!" Thirty minutes later I was lying fully clothed on the bed "receiving" Jin Shin Jyutsu from Charles as he and my husband visited. He wasn't even paying that much attention; he was talking to Allain as he put his hands on two different places, like my neck and arm, then he would move a hand to another place. Within 15 minutes of this treatment I "knew" something special was happening to my body. I fought back the tears of relief that tried to well up. I certainly was not going to cry in front of these two men!

My life changed in that hour. Charles returned two days later to give me one more treatment. After those two hours of Jin Shin Jyutsu I felt better than I had in two years. Two months later I received Mary Burmeister's first self-help book, and began the life-changing process of teaching myself how to do this. Aches and pains and headaches all began diminishing. That was 1984. I have been a student and practitioner of this Art ever since, and was fortunate to attend six of the classes taught by Mary Burmeister.

If the use of Jin Shin Jyutsu is life enhancing, harmonizing, energizing and pain relieving, it sounds like something useful for the living. So what inspired me to write a book about Jin Shin Jyutsu for those who are dying? Because the need is there. The final phase of life can become complicated and confusing for the patient, family members and the medical professionals involved. Often very difficult decisions are required. Often family members are not ready to accept dying as a part of life's process. Doctors and nurses are trained to be caring and to save lives. But hospitals are now big business, and the system begins to intrude on care. Nurses are required to spend much of their valuable time putting medical records on computers; fear of litigation is omnipresent and influences many decisions; often the care givers are overworked and understaffed. A nurse who has been teaching for 22 years tells me of patients and families who feel at an emotional loss with no one to turn to when the "Do Not Resuscitate" order goes up. As I said, this can be a sad, complicated and confusing time. No one has prepared us for it.

Some hospitals have sections specifically designated for dying patients and their families. Doctors are becoming more aware of the benefits of Hospice care and more families are able to take advantage of the invaluable services Hospice provides. The atmosphere is totally different in these situations, where staff members are trained in palliative care and are there to serve the needs of dying patients and their families, whether in the hospital setting or at home. Those who find themselves in these situations are indeed fortunate.

The purpose of this book is to give you some sense of empowerment when the one you love is dying. There is something you can do for your loved one. You are not helpless in this situation. Family members can have a purposeful involvement in the process of death. Even in the midst of the turmoil, you can be truly present, you can find your courage and your own inner strength and with the help of Jin Shin Jyutsu you can give this calmness and peace to the one you care for.

Over and over, with clients and with friends, I have seen the beneficial effects of Jin Shin Jyutsu on both the dying person and his or her family. The stories in this book verify and expand my personal experiences. We are all confronted with death. We have no training for this experience. It can be an anguishing, terrifying time, or it can be a time of calmness and gentleness and peace. I choose the latter. That is why I have written this book.

It will be helpful to have some awareness of the Art of Jin Shin Jyutsu (pronounced: gin shin jit-sue) as you read this book. Jin Shin Jyutsu offers a simple way of using your hands and your breath to help restore emotional equilibrium, to relieve pain, and to release some of the causes of both acute and chronic conditions. The suggestions in this book are in no way limited to use only on the critically ill. They are helpful and life enhancing, and are used daily by practitioners of this Art all over the world. They have been chosen for this book because they are the simpler holds and can be done under difficult circumstances by people who know very little, if anything, about Jin Shin Jyutsu. And they are very effective.

Jin Shin Jyutsu is based on the concept of life energy that circulates throughout the universe and within each individual organism. Your health and energy depend on the free and even distribution of this life energy throughout your body, mind and spirit. With the stresses and strains of daily living — the worries, the fears, the anger, sadness, or when you try too hard to force life in one direction or another — the movement of life energy becomes blocked in various places. You then feel increasingly stiff, achy, ill and "out of balance."

Jin Shin Jyutsu is a way of balancing this life energy. The purpose of Jin Shin Jyutsu is to release the tensions that cause various physical symptoms. Its application is the gentle, non-invasive touch of hands to different areas of the body. This touch can be used on oneself or on another, with the hands placed directly onto the skin, placed over clothes, or even over a cast. It does not involve massage, manipulation of bones or muscles or the use of drugs or substances. It is a valuable complement to conventional healing methods, as it induces relaxation and reduces the effects of stress.

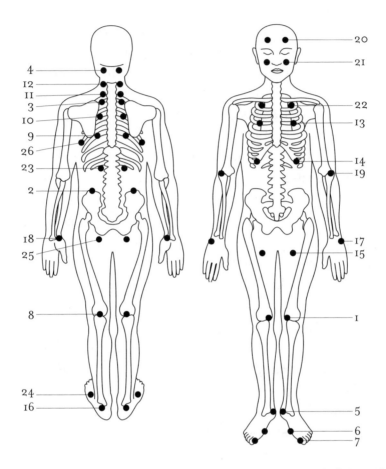

Jin Shin Jyutsu utilizes 26 "Safety Energy Locks" (SELs) mirrored on either side of the body. These safety energy locks, spheres of energy rather than "points," act as circuit breakers to protect the body when the flow of life energy is blocked. This life energy flows along pathways or channels throughout the body. When one or more of these pathways becomes blocked, this damming effect may lead to discomfort or pain. In the process of utilizing Jin Shin Jyutsu, the practitioner touches two of these safety energy locks at one time and waits to feel simultaneous pulses, thereby clearing a portion of the energy pathway. The work of Jin Shin Jyutsu is cumulative; the more the pathways are cleared, the more in harmony the body becomes. This harmony promotes healing. Jin Shin Jyutsu is considered an Art, as opposed to a technique, because once you learn the basic concepts, its application becomes a skillful creation rather than a mechanical application.

Each of the true stories in this book illustrates some particular use of Jin Shin Jyutsu with a person who is critically ill. Since most of the stories were written by practitioners of this Art, they often refer to holding some "number," which refers to a safety energy lock. In the final chapter explanations and descriptions of many of these places on the body and the ways of holding them are presented. The Jin Shin Jyutsu described here is simple and anyone so inclined can become capable of using it.

What is the source of this Art? This "Creative Art of Compassionate Man," a centuries old tradition of acupressure, is an ancient Art born of innate wisdom and passed down from generation to generation by word of mouth. Awareness of this Art had been all but forgotten in Japan until the early 1900s when Jiro Murai rediscovered the essence of this work.

Jiro Murai, born into a lineage of medical physicians including his father and his brother, found himself drawn more to research and philosophy than to pure science. While still a young man, Murai recovered from a critical illness by using ancient healing hand positions, breathing, and fasting he had discovered during his studies. As a result of this recovery, he decided to dedicate the remaining 50 years of his life to the study of the ancient ways of healing. He devoted himself to the research and development of Jin Shin Jyutsu, gathering insight from a range of experiences and resources, including the Bible, ancient Chinese, Greek and Indian texts, and the Kojiki (Japanese Record of Ancient Things). In the 1940s Master Murai took Mary Iino, a young Japanese-American woman studying and working in Japan, as his student. She studied with him for six years before returning to the United States to marry Gil Burmeister and begin a family. Mary Iino Burmeister spent the rest of her life studying and sharing this beautiful gift.

Because of the mushrooming interest in Jin Shin Jyutsu, there are now trained instructors teaching Jin Shin Jyutsu® Physio-Philosophy around the world. Further information regarding Jin Shin Jyutsu, available books, and a description of 5-Day Classes, Self-Help Classes, and Seminars can be found on the website: www.jsjinc.net

Judith B. Andry
New Orleans, LA
August 2008

Forward

As we reach out to hold and cradle our loved ones who are in the process of dying, we are reminded of the simplicity that resides within the Art of Jin Shin Jyutsu, and its ability to restore harmony and peace. Judy Andry has given us an inspiring collection of stories contributed by people who have used Jin Shin Jyutsu to ease the way for those who are at the threshold of their passing on. As clearly expressed through the following stories, practicing the Art of Jin Shin Jyutsu during times of critical need can help restore emotional, physical and spiritual harmony so that one can make the transition in the most peaceful way possible. All of us who are daunted by the sense of responsibility we feel in being present to such a momentous event, are again awakened to the essence of Jin Shin Jyutsu. By simply being, we can hold a Safety Energy Lock, or a finger, and witness the release and peace that unfolds for others and for ourselves.

It is fitting that the publication of *A Touching Good-Bye* coincides with the year of my mother's passing. I can think of no greater testament to the purpose of this book than the remarkable serenity and ease Mary demonstrated at the time of her transition. A heartfelt thanks to Judy for compiling these stories, so that others can also be reminded of the precious gift we have been given through the Art of Jin Shin Jyutsu.

David Burmeister
Jin Shin Jyutsu, Inc.

1

Struggling with Death

The one you love is dying. You are in and out of the room; you hover by the bed; you sit restlessly in a chair nearby. At a loss for words, you reach for a hand, wishing for all the world you knew something better to do that might ease the suffering, soften the pain, calm the fear. You want so much to provide comfort, reassurance, but you don't know how. Whether at home or in the hospital, the trappings of illness are a barrier — the bandages, the I.V. lines, the oxygen tanks. You are daunted. You feel ill equipped in this devastating situation.

The dying person, too, is often anxious and confused about what is happening. He or she is in pain or is fearful of pain, is tense in defense against the unknowable, and unable to let down that guard to allow the body to relax. Your being there, your love and your presence, are a comfort, though the tensions don't abate. You find you are drawn to reach out and touch this person, on the hand, on the arm. That gesture is intuitively correct, because touch brings with it an immediate intimacy, a connective bond. You hesitate; you are not sure if or how this helps, but you know deep in the recesses of your heart this touching connection is important.

The Art of Jin Shin Jyutsu is the art of touch. The stories that unfold here illustrate the benefits of this uncomplicated and compassionate Art. If you are so inclined, you can learn it easily. Using these simple ways of touching, you can bring calm and comfort to the person in need, and in the process you will discover the grace you receive by giving it.

I begin with my own story of that agonizing dilemma we all face at one time or another, when someone we love is close to death: what can I do to "save" this person? I don't want this person to die. I'm not ready for this person to die.

My husband and I had planned a trip, so were away from New Orleans when our friend, Sandy, went into the hospital for heart surgery. In her 60s, she had already outlived her parents and her brother, all of whom had died of heart-related illnesses. Her condition was now serious enough to make surgery imperative. Although her doctors considered the successful outcome of this operation to be highly probable, she approached it with some trepidation. She took pains to get her house in order, even making sure she signed her recently completed oil paintings.

To the relief of all concerned, the complicated heart surgery seemed to be a complete success. Within a few hours, though, monitoring devices began indicating grave problems. Sandy was rushed back into the operating room and her chest was reopened. It was to no avail. Sandy's body was having a total allergic reaction to the chemicals necessary for this type of surgery. She was put on life sustaining machines. Every effort was made to overcome this invasive problem. The prognosis was grim.

When Allain and I arrived home from our trip we heard a frantic message on our answering machine from Sandy's daughter. Lisa had taken classes in Jin Shin Jyutsu in the past and felt she had benefited from the treatments she had received. She felt certain there was some way this could help her mother and she was doing all she knew how to do. Lisa was asking me to come to the hospital. We called and said we were on our way. I tried desperately to think of exactly what Jin Shin Jyutsu help I could bring to a situation that was so obviously critical.

Family and friends had gathered at the hospital for several days. The mood was somber and sad, tinged with disbelief. A decision had to be made about the life support systems. The minister was enroute. Sandy's husband and three young adult children were there.

Lisa approached me with grateful relief in her eyes, hopeful. I felt totally inadequate to the situation. What on earth could I do to "save" Sandy? What on earth could I do, period? We went into the room where Sandy lay on the hospital bed, hooked to various machines. Her eyes fluttered but did not open and her hand moved when Lisa told her I was there. I gently held Sandy's hand and did the Jin Shin Jyutsu method of holding each finger. Lisa slipped her hand behind the back of her mother's head, cradling the #4s,[1] continuing a Jin Shin Jyutsu hold she had been using off and on for several days. We quietly held these positions.

---

1. Safety Energy Lock (SEL) #4s are the two knotty protrusions where the back of the neck meets the skull.

I was anxious, wondering what else could be done. What could help Sandy in this critical situation? I knew I was not God, yet I have strong faith in the powers of Jin Shin Jyutsu. Was there some miraculous placement of hands I just wasn't remembering? I moved down to her toes, holding them one by one. After about 20 minutes other friends began coming in to say good-bye. The minister had arrived. It was time to face the difficult decision about the machines.

This was an intimate family time. We said good-bye and my husband and I sadly drove home. Sandy died quietly and peacefully, surrounded by her family only a short time after the life support systems were removed.

༶ ༶ ༶

Besides being grieved over our friend's death, I was disturbed by questions regarding my understanding of Jin Shin Jyutsu and the effectiveness of its use in life and death situations. I had, until now, found the use of this Art to be life giving, energizing, a powerful life force. In the face of death, was it useless, or worse, not to be used? As I researched this question, the answer became clearer to me. There is life energy throughout the universe and within each individual organism. In humans this life energy is present at the moment of conception. We recognize this energy in the breath that comes with birth and we know it is what supports our system until death, which is marked by the departure of this life force energy. The use of Jin Shin Jyutsu acupressure balances this energy, allowing it to move harmoniously throughout the body by removing the blockages that lead to mental, physical and emotional disharmony. In the final stages of life, this special type of touch is used to bring harmony to the body as much as possible and to support the life system as it begins its final transition.

My agony about "what to do" at the time of Sandy's death came from a lack of awareness on my part. I realize now there is no specific "way to be" with a dying person. Accepting our own fears of being inadequate, accepting the humility of "I don't know" when faced with an experience we cannot know, are essential parts of this process. What I did not realize was the powerful, positive effect Jin Shin Jyutsu has on both the dying patient and the family members and caregivers who make use of it. Fortunately, Lisa knew this in her heart and had been doing exactly the right things, which is probably why her mother died so peacefully when the life-support systems were removed. The issue, in the end, was not about saving Sandy, it was about being present, consciously present, for her transition, and being aware there was something specific each family member could actually do at the time of this crossover. Lisa instinctively understood, and was able to achieve this for her mother and for her family.

I am now aware that in anyone's hour of need there are very simple, yet very powerful tools any of us can use which bring calmness, consolation, and peace to another. These tools are at our fingertips.

A Touching Good-Bye

Mitzi Adams, a Jin Shin Jyutsu practitioner in Connecticut, experienced a similar struggle with death. When her mother suffered a heart attack, Mitzi went through the agonies of not wanting to lose her. Mitzi made every effort to save her mother with the use of Jin Shin Jyutsu. In the end she, like me, learned a valuable lesson. Here is Mitzi's story:

On a Friday in 1994 my mother suffered a heart attack. All of the family began gathering. On Saturday my sister and I arrived at the hospital. We began doing Jin Shin Jyutsu nonstop on our mother with the intent of saving her.

On Monday morning our minister called the family into another room, preparing us for her imminent death. I stayed in the room with Mom, continuing to give her Jin Shin Jyutsu. Sitting at her bedside, on her left side, I was holding what I could conveniently reach. I had slipped my left hand under her left side so that it was gently touching the top of her left pelvic bone, and my right hand was cradled behind her head, holding her #4s. I was praying all the while for her to live. I didn't want to believe she was going to die and I was desperately "trying to"[2] jump-start her heart. It was my mission to utilize Jin Shin Jyutsu to rescue her.

When the family re-entered the room, and after the minister's final prayers, we finally surrendered and let God take over. Everyone quietly "jumper cabled"[3] her, holding

---

2. "Trying to" is an indication of too much attempt to force life.
3. When placed in the appropriate places one's hands act like jumper cables as the life energy flows through them.

her fingers, toes and the back of her head. We felt, in our small way that we helped her to pass more peacefully.

This experience with my mother's passing led me to a whole new way of thinking about death and dying. A Divine Plan was at work and the Jin Shin Jyutsu was merely supporting it. The result is not from personal "doing." I am only a conduit. Unbeknownst to me, this was an important lesson I was to use in the coming months.

*+ *+ *+

A few months later Mitzi was unexpectedly confronted with another life and death situation.

It is helpful when reading this story to understand that, when close to death, some people experience lifelike dreams or visions, some of which may be pleasant and some of which may be frightening. The person Mitzi helped had one of these experiences.

At a church service four months after my mother's death, a man asked the congregation to pray for his father, James, who had just been told he had two weeks to live. After church service I told him about Jin Shin Jyutsu and said that, though there were no guarantees, I'd be willing to work with his father. He agreed and within the week we had a session scheduled.

His father was in the end stage of liver failure. Twenty years prior, he had suffered a heart attack, which required several surgeries and blood transfusions. It was at that time he contracted Hepatitis C, precipitating 20 years of liver "projects."[4] Just recently he had been rushed to Yale New Haven Hospital where he underwent a procedure that redirected the blood flow through his liver. Complications arose after the first attempt, indicating the procedure would have to be performed again. Due to his weakened condition, however, the physicians deemed further surgery too risky. It was at this point I began my work with James. The day he arrived at my office, he was freezing cold from his failing vascular system, and was bloated with excess body fluid. Seeing this man helped me recall the lesson I had learned at my mother's death. It was not up to me to try to "save" anyone. I put this man's life in God's hands. With a silent prayer and this understanding, I began my "jumper-cabling."

By his second treatment, the excess fluid had disappeared from his body. Among other things, I did the #23/25 Flow[5] for bloating. By the third session, still within the first week, he had dramatically changed. During our session in the second week we experienced something extraordinary. He was lying on my table and my hands were holding his #4s, when he said, "There are people in the room, hovering there, in the corner. They're dressed like monks. They are saying, 'James, this is not your time.'" Immediately thereafter, I felt a vibrating energy coming up

---

4. To consider an issue a project rather than a problem allows the idea that a certain amount of time and focused energy may result in a positive outcome.
5. An explanation of the #23/25 Flow is found in *Text Book I*, which is used when taking a Jin Shin Jyutsu 5-Day Class. A less complex hold for bloating is described in Chapter 8.

from my feet, through my body, into my hands and passing through to James.

When I asked him later about what had happened during that Jin Shin Jyutsu session, he simply said, "I want to save it and put in my pocket." Neither he nor his wife ever shared his Jin Shin Jyutsu experiences with his doctors. That was in 1995. He continues to come for regular Jin Shin Jyutsu sessions and he walks nearly five miles every day. [6]

*+ *+ *+

How can it be that some people die and others have unexplainable recoveries? It is a mystery. None of us have power over the life or death of another person, over saving or not saving, over living or dying. That realm is much bigger than we are. We are here, in this time of need, to love that person and to provide as much comfort as we possibly can.

Mitzi and I already had been studying the use of Jin Shin Jyutsu, so at least we were familiar with it when we were called upon to help someone in need. Doyle, on the other hand, had never taken a class in Jin Shin Jyutsu when she was asked to help her friend, Paul, who worked for the State Department.

My friend Paul was dying. He had been diagnosed with AIDS the previous year and now he had pneumocystis, the killer pneumonia that decimates so many people with the AIDS virus. His doctor had told him there was no possibility of his survival unless he went into the hospital for treatment. Paul, though, was adamant in his refusal to be hospitalized. He stated point blank that if his fate was

---

6. James lived for ten more years.

to die, then he would die. He didn't want to suffer the helplessness and indignity of hospitalization.

Mary Burmeister had helped Paul greatly the preceding year when he was diagnosed with AIDS. At the time of the diagnosis, Paul's t-cell count was very low. Mary found that his Safety Energy Lock #4s were closing, a life threatening condition, and she was able to reverse this process. Sure enough, Paul felt better and was able to survive an extended business trip to a third-world country, a trip his doctor had told him would almost certainly be fatal.

Now it was a year later and Paul had pneumocystis. He and I had plans to go to a JSJ[7] class, but it was obvious that Paul would be too ill to travel. He had already taken JSJ classes several times, but it was to be my first class. So even though I wasn't familiar with Jin Shin, he suggested I come over and give him some flows.[8] He said I could use his books and he would show me what to do.

I arrived at a scene from hell. Paul's apartment was sweltering, but he couldn't get warm. He was burning up with temperature — about 104°F; he coughed incessantly; he hadn't eaten for days. Fortunately, his friend, Mark, had come for a visit and had stayed to help out when Paul got sick. At Paul's direction, I did several JSJ flows (#3, #13, and 3rd Method of Correction)[9] over the next few hours. Throughout, Mark and I kept cracking jokes to keep from crying. This made Paul laugh and precipitated terrible

---

7. Jin Shin Jyutsu.

8. Touching a series of sites along a particular energy pathway.

9. Though these flows are not germane to this book, I leave them in for the sake of those already knowledgeable about this work. Simpler flows are described in the final chapter.

coughing fits. But we couldn't stop doing it and I think Paul rather enjoyed it.

I left in a state of great sorrow, wondering just how much longer Paul could live and whether Mark and I had done the right thing by not forcing him to enter the hospital. I had been home about half an hour when, to my astonishment, Paul called. He said, "I feel great. The fever's gone; and I'm eating a banana." I was completely stunned; so was Mark. We had witnessed something that "couldn't happen." Paul rapidly improved, and we were able to go to the JSJ class together.

Paul lived for almost four more years. He did JSJ on himself regularly; he went twice a year to Scottsdale to receive treatments from Mary; and I worked on him whenever we were together. For the last two years of his life he had zero t-cells, yet he didn't get sick. He lived a full life, pursuing his interests until the end. The process of his dying was a remarkable example for all who knew him.

༚ ༚ ༚

Life or death? To live or to die? That decision is not up to us, the caregivers, the givers of the Art of Jin Shin Jyutsu. Each individual makes that decision, either consciously or unconsciously. The use of Jin Shin Jyutsu near the time of death brings calmness and harmony to the body, which seems to allow that spiritual and transcendent decision to be more easily made.

Calmness and reduction of tension, the hallmarks of this Art of Jin Shin Jyutsu, seem to provide a space within a person for individual transitions to take place. I once had a woman come to me for a Jin Shin Jyutsu session, a stranger who had been referred by a friend. After the hour session, during which time we barely spoke, she sat up, and remained sitting quietly on the side of the Jin Shin Jyutsu table. I was standing silently behind her. After a full minute of silence she said, almost to herself, "My life will never be the same." She put on her shoes, paid her fee, and walked out. I never saw her again.

Most Jin Shin Jyutsu practitioners respect the privacy of their clients and do not ask for explanations of the results of the treatments. Sometimes, especially in the case of physical ailments, the results are obvious. Other times, as in the case of the woman above, the effects are very private. With the stories in this book, however, of people in their last stages of life, the effects of this acupressure Art arc not only obvious, they are quietly inspiring and dramatic.

2

CALMING ANGER AND FEARS

The anger. Where does one go with the anger? The anger of "it's not my time." The anger behind "Why me?" The anger at the indignity of what this illness is doing to my body. The anger I feel toward the doctor, the hospital, the insurance people. What do I do with the anger about the disappointments in my life, the grudges and resentments that linger? How and where do I place the blame for this happening now, at this time, to me and to the people I love? I'm not ready for this. They are not ready for this.

And creeping up right behind the anger is the fear. What's going to happen? I'm terrified of not knowing. I don't want to be diminished. I'm fearful of the pain, now and as it intensifies. How will I bear this? How do I face the possibility of death? Often medication is prescribed, and often it helps. But sometimes the medication makes me feel I am losing control of myself. How do I maintain my dignity? Is it possible there is another approach to dealing with these devastating issues?

A Touching Good-Bye

Susan Brooks is a Jin Shin Jyutsu instructor with a practice in Colorado. Her experience, and the ones that follow, help to answer these pervasive questions. Is it possible there is an alternative and complimentary approach to dealing with these anger and fear issues?

A friend asked me to visit his aunt who was in a nursing home. The nursing home was having a very difficult time with her. She was, to put it mildly, an irascible curmudgeon. She was deaf, she had cataracts in both eyes, and she was very angry. She had never married, nor had she ever experienced a gentle and loving touch. She was filled with resentment towards life. In her anger she threw things at her attendants and visitors, and often had to be tied to her wheelchair or restrained in bed.

I began giving her Jin Shin Jyutsu treatments twice a week. I was pleased as slowly a trust and rapport developed between us. That happened, I think, because Jin Shin Jyutsu is gentle and non-invasive. It is not frightening or manipulative in any way. She came to enjoy our sessions, insisting on removing all of her clothes for them, even though Jin Shin Jyutsu treatments are traditionally done with clothes on. She had a great resentment about her life, and especially about her mother. As I worked with her I began to feel some of this anger and resentment melt away. Her habit of throwing things at anyone who walked in the door slowly abated.

One day I received a call from the nursing home telling me her end was near. When I arrived her breathing was labored and slow. I didn't know if she would realize I was there as I began doing the fingers and toes flow.[1] It became obvious she could tell because she would gently respond with her hands. To my amazement she sat up and put her arms around me and said, "Mama." This happened three times during our session. She sat up, held me, and said, "Mama." It was obvious her anger had been released. She then communicated to me by letting go of my hand that it was time for our session to be over. Her hand just went limp. It was obvious to me she was done with receiving. She died an hour later.

I went to her room in the nursing home the next morning. All of her things had been removed, the room cleaned. The window was open, the curtains blowing in the breeze. I felt her spirit and it felt free.

When I think of her experience of Jin Shin Jyutsu, I think of the trust that developed, the anger that melted, and the love she felt that was finally able to come through. It has been my experience in working with dying people that they are able to be very clear when they no longer need the Jin Shin Jyutsu. This is a consistent theme. I call it "God speaking."

༚ ༚ ༚

Fear, bordering on terror, is an emotion often exhibited by those close to death. I have sat with people who are agitated and distressed by terrifying visions in their heads. What a gift you give if you find a way to ease these terrors for a dying person. Bill Thames is a Jin Shin Jyutsu practitioner in Dallas. His intuition told him to go to the hospital, where Bill was confronted with his friend's intense fear.

---

1. A description of the fingers and toes flow is in Chapter 8.

Steve was diagnosed with a very rare form of leukemia and was hospitalized. He was near death. This was at night. The next morning some voice within me says, "Go see Steve." My rational mind says, "Oh, you can go tomorrow." The inner voice says, "You will go today!" I went.

When I arrived at his bedside I found Steve nervous and terrified, not knowing what was happening. His eyes were bugging out; he was gasping for breath; he had lost his voice. He must have known he was near death. My hand automatically went to the outer side of his left wrist,[2] which helps nerves and chaos in the body. In a few minutes he began calming down and his breathing became normal. He tried to talk; I felt he was trying to say thank you. I offered him a drink of water so that in supporting his head to drink, I could have an opportunity to hold his #4s. I held these for about five minutes as a doctor came and went. Then Steve's niece arrived. "I'll go since you are here," I said. "Call me if I can help further." I had been home about 30 minutes when his niece called. Steve had just died. She told me, "After you left he laid back in his bed and I quietly played one of his favorite opera recordings. He was calm, and he left in such a peaceful state."

࿊ ࿊ ࿊

---

2. SEL #17.

A Touching Good-Bye

Connie White lives and practices Jin Shin Jyutsu in San Antonio, Texas. Her story illustrates the powerful effects of only a small amount of Jin Shin Jyutsu.

My friend Barbara called. Her husband was very ill and had asked if I would come over. Karl was 84, a Reiki Master,[3] and had long been a believer in alternative medicine. He wanted to see if Jin Shin Jyutsu could help.

When I arrived he was sitting up in a chair. He was extremely thin and pale and explained to me he had been unable to keep any food down for many days. Even water would gag him. I suggested he seriously consider going to the hospital. He would probably die if he did not. Karl realized he was dying and did not want to go to the hospital. He confessed the process of dying was more uncomfortable than he had anticipated, and he felt afraid even though he knew better. Did I know anything to help him with his fear? I said I did.

While he remained sitting in his chair I did the Bladder Flow.[4] I felt him slowly relaxing, then he fell asleep. With a sigh of gratitude Barbara explained he had been restless and agitated and unable to sleep for days. She thanked me and asked what I thought was happening and how long it would take for him to die. I told her I would be surprised if he lasted the night.

Early the next morning the phone rang and it was Barbara saying Karl had died during the night. I remembered

---

3. A Japanese healing art.
4. The Bladder Function Energy Flow is one of the JSJ Organ Flows, found in *Text Book II*, and is taught in the JSJ 5-Day Class. For the purposes of this book there are simpler flows given in Chapter 8.

several times Mary saying the Bladder Flow had to do with fear of the unknown, and when someone was holding on to life because of fear of moving on, it was a tremendous help to open the bladder meridian. It certainly appears to have worked in Karl's case. He had never before experienced the touch of Jin Shin Jyutsu. It was the last resort. I was just a friend willing to share Mary Burmeister's gift with a neighbor. What a blessing Jin Shin Jyutsu has been for me.

෴ ෴ ෴

In 1992 Jeanette Pasqua, who lives in Pennsylvania, attended her first Jin Shin Jyutsu class. Her Mother-in-law had recently been diagnosed with an HIV infection from a tainted blood transfusion. At this time the HIV medicine "cocktail" was not yet available, and her diagnosis was terrifying.

Philomena Dooley was my instructor and this class filled me with awe and hope. After the 5-Day Class I asked Philomena if she thought Jin Shin Jyutsu could help my mother-in-law, Eileen. She assured me the Art of Jin Shin Jyutsu is a harmonizer and she thought it would be helpful. We made appointments for Mom to receive several sessions with Philomena. At these sessions, Philomena encouraged me to "get to work" and offered the special #23 flow and the toe flows[5] for Eileen's project. Philomena urged me to just go for it and treat Mom on a regular basis.

It is really amazing how life offers you these opportunities for learning and growth. I felt I didn't know

---

5. The Special 23 Flow and the Kidney, Liver, Spleen "Toe" Flows are taught in the Jin Shin Jyutsu 5-Day Class.

enough to help her, yet here I was offering Mom sessions and intensives, two sessions a day for five days. It was such an honor for me to share in this experience with her. Mom said that after each intensive, she had so much more energy and less fear. After her last intensive, she went home and wallpapered her laundry room till the wee hours of the morning. We laughed about that. "It just felt so good to feel energized and I couldn't stop once I got started," she said.

Mom felt anxious and fearful at times. This period was filled with a lot of misinformation and fearful spin about HIV. Most of her friends rallied around her, but there were a few who felt too frightened and left. Throughout it all, she shared that she felt a sense of peace and ease after her sessions of Jin Shin Jyutsu. She was a faithful practitioner of her self-help "homework." Early in her self-help practice, I found Mom in the kitchen standing in front of a chair with her leg propped up on it. She had the oven timer on and was giving herself a spleen flow.[6] When I asked her why she had the oven timer on, she replied, "I wanted to do it right." We had a good laugh together then, too.[7] Eventually she settled into the lazy boy chair and practiced her toe flows daily along with the Main Central.[8]

Mom lived for another four years and finally the virus crossed into her brain. We cared for her at her home and when asked if she wanted a session, she would almost always

---

6. One of the 12 Organ Flows in Jin Shin Jyutsu.
7. Jin Shin Jyutsu is considered an Art because there are no set rules. Jeanette's mother soon realized she could hold a position just as long as it felt right.
8. The Main Central is the primary harmonizing energy flow in the body. A description for doing the Main Central as self-help can be found in Chapter 8.

answer, "Yes, please." It was a different experience for her to have sessions during this time. She seemed freer knowing that she was passing. She shared that she looked forward to the Jin Shin Jyutsu sessions, that it felt like she was soaking it up. When Mom was near death and unconscious, I held her #4s and left ring finger. It seemed to help her relax and allowed her to breathe more easily.

Our family gathered around Mom's bedside to be with her the night before she died. Like many people, she waited to die until we'd all left and gone home for the night. Someone from the hospital called at 8:00 A.M. the next morning to say she had passed away.

The experience taught me so much that I draw upon still. I learned not to have expectations when jumper cabling. When giving a session I do my best to be present, to be aware of my breath and feel the energies shift. The rest is really bigger than all of us. I've shared in so many incredible moments, each unique, from birth to death and everything in between. We are so very blessed.

✛✛ ✛✛ ✛✛

Our anger and fears are serious consequences of illness and imminent death. We all have to deal with them one way or another. Is it possible this simple Art of Jin Shin Jyutsu could actually help? Is it worth trying?

3

Easing Physical

and Emotional Pain

I was introduced to Jin Shin Jyutsu at age 47, when neck and shoulder pain had finally turned into total body aching 24 hours a day. As I mentioned in the Introduction, within 15 minutes of receiving my first Jin Shin Jyutsu session I "knew" something right and helpful was happening to my body. Now, 24 years later, being a witness to my own positive experience and to those of countless others, I reiterate: easing of pain is a hallmark of this Art of Jin Shin Jyutsu. Understand, too, one can be in emotional pain that is equally as debilitating as physical pain. Often, the two are combined. While physical and emotional pains are sometimes present in our busy and stress filled lives, these can become overpowering during critical illness, both for the patient and for the caregiver.

Al Canner, in finding physical relief from his own pain, was able to help his mother while finding a new path for his life as well. Al had learned over the years to live with the migraine headaches he had suffered from the age of nine. During his 40s, though, when they turned into debilitating cluster headaches, he began a serious search for relief. A friend recommended Jin Shin Jyutsu. He made an appointment with Susan Brooks and began treatments once a week. Al also had another medical issue, an aortic valve insufficiency, wherein the valve doesn't close correctly, forcing some blood to backflow. The heart slowly enlarges to compensate for its inefficacious pumping. This is a potentially serious condition, but since Al was athletically inclined and in good physical shape, it was not causing him discomfort. The cardiologist had monitored the aortic valve for 15 years with annual echocardiograms. Now, though Al was not experiencing any discomfort, the incremental increases in heart size were reaching a potentially dangerous level. His cardiologist was recommending valve surgery in the next few years.

When Al began going to Susan for his headache treatments he mentioned his aortic valve condition. After about six months of Jin Shin Jyutsu it happened to be time for his annual echocardiogram. The cardiologist sounded puzzled when he called with the results. Al's heart size had retreated to the less threatening size it had been four years previously. The cardiologist acknowledged he had never seen this happen before and had absolutely no explanation for it. Al told his cardiologist the only change in his life was that he was receiving Jin Shin Jyutsu treatments. The cardiologist said to keep doing whatever worked. Al's heart has remained this safe size for the last seven years.

While his echocardiogram was bringing good news, there was sad news in Florida. Al's mother was diagnosed with pancreatic cancer and underwent surgery. In his rush to get to his mother, Al was able to obtain from Susan instructions on how to do the Jin Shin Jyutsu finger holds. At this point Al had been receiving Jin Shin Jyutsu for six months. He had learned a few places to touch himself for self-help, but he had taken no classes and had not studied it in any way. He recognized the changes Jin Shin Jyutsu had made in his body, though, and felt confident this would benefit his mother.

When I arrived in Florida I found there was much anxiety associated with Mother's diagnosis of cancer, with questions about her operation, her caregivers, and where she would live now that she was so ill. I sat by her side and gently began the hand and finger hold Susan had taught me. I held her right hand with my left hand, and with my right hand I began holding her thumb. As I quietly talked to her I progressed slowly from finger to finger until I finished by holding her little finger. She loved it. She began to relax, and from that moment until her death, she responded extremely positively to any Jin Shin Jyutsu she received. What surprised me the most was the empowerment I felt while doing this for my mother. In her illness and her anxiety, in the hospital setting, or in any setting, here was something I could actually do that would bring her solace and relief. There is something wonderful about this touch connection. It is neither sentimental nor clawing. It is a gentle touch with a purpose, and both the person giving it and the person receiving it seem to automatically "know" something good and "right" is happening. I was truly amazed at what this did for both my mother and for me.

Diagnosed with pancreatic cancer, my mother was given about three months to live. My wife and I wanted her to come live with us in Colorado, but she did not want to impose her illness on her grandson, our five-year-old son. We contacted Hospice. She lived at home in Florida with the invaluable aid of the Hospice workers and a caring and loving nephew. This was our first introduction to Hospice and we will be forever grateful for its help and kindness.

After a month-and-a-half in Florida, Mother consented to come and live with us. As we were getting her comfortably settled, she saw our young son, Leo, peep around the door, then disappear. We feared she was seeing what she had dreaded: her grandson fearful and disturbed by her condition. Thirty minutes later, though, Leo bounced into the room, climbed onto the bed, laughed and talked with her until dinnertime, then insisted she must sit next to him. He also insisted his name be signed on the Hospice papers as one of the caregivers. In the middle of one night when Leo crawled into the bed with her, she stayed awake all night just to savor the experience.

My mother lived another three-and-a-half weeks. I did Jin Shin Jyutsu with her every day. She was always accepting and appreciative of these sessions. Ten days before her death, Susan Brooks came to give her a treatment. Mother was sitting in a chair. I remember being touched by the beauty of that encounter. Mother sitting in the chair with Susan bending over her, first on one side, and then the other. It resembled a ballet. I cannot emphasize enough the quietness and gentleness of Jin Shin Jyutsu. I think Susan's treatment was a subtle turning point for my mother. After that she seemed to cooperate with her decline rather than resist it. Although she never spoke about it, I feel it liberated her in some way that allowed her to let go and die.

In the last days of her life she was unconscious. At that point the Jin Shin Jyutsu I used was to simply slide my hand under the back of her head, with the other hand holding one of her fingers. It seemed to sooth her breathing, and again, it was such an empowering way for me to be with my mother. It gave me such a sense that what I was doing was benefiting her. Towards the end I would do this for hours at a time. She died quietly in the night. My wife and brother and I were taking shifts to be with her near the end. I was fortunate to be with her in the final moments. It was very moving. We are forever grateful for the grace that Hospice and Jin Shin Jyutsu brought to the last three months of my mother's life.

After my mother's death and after experiencing the final three months of her illness, I began seriously to reconsider my life direction. I was a practicing attorney and now I wanted to do something more immediately humane and relational. The care the Hospice workers had provided for my mother and for us during her illness, both in Florida and in Colorado, had made an indelible impression on me. They had taught my wife, son, and me how to be with my dying mother. I invited the local Hospice director to lunch to thank her for all Hospice had done for our family. She informed me this was the final week of accepting applications for the job of Executive Director of the Colorado Hospice organization. I applied.

Now in his seventh year as Executive Director of the Colorado Hospice Organization, Al has, on several occasions, asked Susan Brooks to give seminars on the use of Jin Shin Jyutsu during Hospice care. She explains ways Jin Shin Jyutsu can be used both for the patient and for the caregiver. People find the use of these suggestions incredibly powerful.

Al, his wife, and his son are devoted Jin Shin Jyutsu users. They have learned a series of uncomplicated self-help holds they use regularly. They also know assorted places to hold if they get sore throats, colds, neck aches, nausea, stomachaches, anxiety, and for strengthening the immune system. Through the age of 12, their son had used antibiotics only three times. For this they credit Jin Shin Jyutsu and homeopathic medicine. The use of Jin Shin Jyutsu has become an integral part of their lives.

I only wish every reader of this book could hear Al's enthusiastic descriptions of Jin Shin Jyutsu. He is totally inspired and inspiring. His acceptance and use of Jin Shin Jyutsu is unusual in that he has never taken a class and does not know, or feel he needs to know, the "numbers" of the Jin Shin Jyutsu places on the body. Susan tells him where to touch for particular reasons, and he just does it and gets results! Because of the simplicity and joy of his family's use of Jin Shin Jyutsu I am including Al's personal self-help list.

AL'S SELF-HELP JIN SHIN JYUTSU[1]

For heart: each day for five minutes hold the left little finger with the right hand, holding snugly with the right thumb in between the fingers where the little finger connects with the hand.

For headaches: hold for five minutes the inner side of the left or the right ankle, midway between the anklebone and the heel, with the fingers of the right hand on the inner side of the ankle "matched" by the fingers of the left hand on the outer side of the ankle. Repeat with the other ankle, retaining the right hand on the inner side of the ankle.

For hay fever: place the fingers of the right hand on the coccyx (the very tip of the tailbone), and place the left hand fingers on the inner side of the left ankle for five minutes. Then change and put the fingers of the left hand on the coccyx and the right hand fingers on the inner side of the right ankle.

To bolster the immune system: Drape the left hand over the right shoulder and press gently where the middle finger falls, while making a circle by putting the right thumb on all four fingernails, one at a time, for several minutes each. Repeat on the other side.

For sore throat: Drape the left hand over the right shoulder and press gently where the middle finger lands, and place the right middle finger on the second rib down from the clavicle on the left side of the body (upper chest). Repeat on the other side.

---

1. Al's Self-Help Jin Shin Jyutsu is repeated in Chapter 8.

For the immune system: Spread the fingers of both hands widely apart and place them on either side of the midpoint on the top of the skull.

For nausea: Place the right hand on the inner side of the left or right knee, and the left hand on the opposite inner knee. Hold these two places at the same time.

For eyes: Hold the base of the middle finger on the same side as the eye with the need.

For the stomach: The double thumb hold: Simultaneously wrap the fingers of one hand around the thumb of the other hand. This is not difficult, but it may take a minute to figure out. With palms facing down and thumbs facing each other, curl your fingers into a loose fist. Now simply slide the right thumb into the left fist and the left thumb into the right fist. Relax with your hands in your lap.

For anxiety: Hold both index fingers with the other fingers.

Once you have figured these out for yourself, you can also do them on someone else. Al emphasizes how soothing Jin Shin Jyutsu was for his mother, and how empowering and comforting it was for him as the caregiver. This theme is repeated often in the stories throughout this book.

There is a postscript to Al's story. Three years later, he did have his aortic valve replaced. His heart had resumed its growth and the time had come for the surgery. Susan treated Al in the hospital and continued to help him through his rapid recovery (hiking in the Colorado high country three months after the surgery). That Al remained asymptomatic right up until the time of the surgery he attributes in significant part to Jin Shin Jyutsu.

Al left his work with Hospice in 2003 and embarked on a two-year hiatus from career pursuits. More than a score of week-long solo camping and hiking trips in the mountains and Utah desert country punctuated his respite. During those meditative hikes, Al surpassed the age at which his father had died. Al's thankful he gave himself time to think about such an incredible and important thing. Al is now a member of the faculty of the University of Colorado Law School, where he teaches education law, legal writing, and appellate advocacy. He continues doing self-help Jin Shin Jyutsu every day.

When faced with critical issues most people want to get their affairs in order. They check their wills, possibly see a minister or priest or rabbi, they make an effort to connect with old friends. A big issue is reconciliation, settling old disputes. The more one is able to set things straight and get things in order, the more peaceful one can be as the illness progresses. In the next story Bill Thames describes an emotional reconnection with his brother.

I'm from a family of ten children, with six brothers and three sisters. I was always closest to my brother, Don, though we had grown apart in the past few months and I hadn't seen him very often. His girlfriend was suspicious of Jin Shin Jyutsu, and although he loved it, I found the situation awkward and stayed away. One day he called and asked for a Jin Shin Jyutsu session, which was uncharacteristic for him. I said sure.

When he arrived and walked into my office dragging his feet and looking ashen, I said, concerned, "You look like death warmed over." It puzzled me when he answered by asking why I hadn't returned his phone call. The story unfolded. Don had been in a serious automobile wreck. His speeding car had hydroplaned and hit a concrete embankment, totally demolishing the car. Astonishingly, he had walked away. His telephone message to me had been accidentally misplaced in our office so I never saw it.

We began a Jin Shin Jyutsu session right away, and talked a lot, because we hadn't seen each other for a while. He continued coming for seven sessions within two weeks, and each time he looked better. While we talked and reconnected he told me he didn't know why he was still here, that he didn't enjoy life anymore. His diabetes limited many of the things he would have liked to do. I tried to offer suggestions of assorted ways to enjoy life.

We had beautiful and happy reminisces of our childhood. We reconnected as brothers and as friends. On what turned out to be our last afternoon session of Jin Shin Jyutsu, I marveled at his even and strong pulses.[2] He felt like a million dollars. The next morning he died. I was told that at the hospital, while the doctors were frantically working on him, Don looked at his son with a big smile and just knocked the doctor's hands away.

When I got the call I immediately began crying and rushed to the hospital. Then I saw his beautiful smile. After that I did not grieve. I knew he was where he wanted to be. This was my closest brother. Surviving that accident gave us the opportunity to reconnect. I now realize Jin Shin Jyutsu can prepare us to stay, or help us go on with a smile on our faces, knowing we are going back to our Spiritual Home, from whence we came.

⁙ ⁙ ⁙

Jane's father was 89 when he returned to his summer home in Colorado in April of 1999. On the trip home to Colorado his health had taken a strong turn for the worse.

He had been in failing health for a number of years, with a heart condition, Alzheimer's, and failing eyesight, but now he was barely able to move or breathe. The next day,

---

2. In Jin Shin Jyutsu one waits to feel a pulsing under the fingertips when touching the different Safety Energy Locks.

acting on the advice of local Hospice, we placed him in the hospital for one night, until we could secure a place for him in a nursing home.

As the nurses tended to his needs and sedated him with morphine, my mother and I searched the town for a nursing home that could take him. Partially successful, we returned to the hospital late that afternoon. My father was in terrible turmoil. He seemed to be fighting a battle we could not see. He was moaning and tossing in his bed. He seemed very anxious to do something, but afraid to do it at the same time. My mother went to his right side and I went to the left side of the bed.

While Mother talked to him, I took his left hand in mine and softly said hello. He recognized both of us and seemed to take comfort in our voices. When I asked if he was all right, he said he was going to die, but he was afraid. Intuitively I grasped his first (index) finger in my hand and held it firmly but gently. In Jin Shin Jyutsu the index finger is connected to the attitude of fear. I told him everything would be just fine, that it was okay to die.

I held his finger for about five minutes and I could see him relax and grow calmer with each minute. He let his head sink back into the pillows and his face became serene. He breathed more evenly and within a few more minutes seemed to be sleeping like a baby. We stayed for a little while longer as he slept until the nurse told us we should probably go home and get some supper and some rest.

About 10:00 p.m. that night the hospital called to tell us my father had passed. They said he had quietly passed in his sleep, very peacefully. I don't know if it was entirely the Jin Shin Jyutsu which helped him, but I do know that I could "feel" or sense the calm come over him as I held his finger and I think it surely helped ease his passing. I am a firm believer in what Jin Shin Jyutsu can do.

﹌﹌﹌

Jane's story makes me think of my brother, Jap, a retired Urologist. He appreciates his occasional Jin Shin Jyutsu sessions, but always goes right to sleep when I begin. He says, "I have to go to sleep because if I stay awake I drive myself crazy trying to figure out medically how and why what you do works!" Can you believe holding the index finger five minutes can actually have the calming effect it had on Jane's father? The only way to know is by trying it yourself, either on yourself or on someone you care for. An explanation on the use of the fingers is found in Chapter 8.

Though we have no way of knowing the extent of a person's inner pain, when using Jin Shin Jyutsu to harmonize the body's energy pathways, tightly held emotions are often released and the body is freed of its tensions. Bill describes the release Bunny experienced.

Bunny was in her late 70s and lived in Ft. Worth. Her daughter-in-law, who lived in New Orleans and had been receiving Jin Shin Jyutsu sessions, thought they might be beneficial for Bunny. She contacted me.

Bunny had such an extreme case of emphysema she was forced to be on oxygen 24 hours a day. After our first session Bunny slept well and said she felt better than she had in a long time. After our second session three days later she said Jin Shin Jyutsu was the only thing that had made her comfortable. We continued with a third session on the following Saturday.

During our fourth session on Monday, as soon as I began working with her, Bunny's hands and feet became knotted and gnarled. It was like she was holding on for dear life. I thought to myself, her Spirit wants to leave but she is not quite ready. She said, "Bill, what is that?" I answered, "I think you know. You tell me." "Oh," she said, "that's what I thought it was." Slowly her hands and feet relaxed. I felt she had been given the idea there was a reason she needed to stay, to clear something up.

Two days later she passed away. At Bunny's funeral this is what her daughter, who is also a client of mine, told me. After that fourth session of Jin Shin Jyutsu, Bunny called this daughter and invited her for a visit. She told me they had a long talk and worked out all of their differences. Then Bunny asked her daughter to take her to the hospital and to call her brother to come from New Orleans. "We all said our good-byes, then Mom laid back in that bed with the most gorgeous smile I'd ever seen. If you don't believe me, ask the mortician. The mortician later told me he had never seen a more beautiful smile than that."

This experience helped the daughter heal also. She has not needed much Jin Shin Jyutsu since then, though she still comes often enough to maintain her body's balance. She has been doing well for the past eight years.

†‡†‡†‡

A Touching Good-Bye

Jill Holden, a Jin Shin Jyutsu instructor and practitioner in California, gives us three examples that offer a new slant on our understanding of life and death, physical pain, and depression.

Susan had ovarian cancer and was in the hospital for a second-look surgery. We had planned for me to come to the hospital to treat her with Jin Shin Jyutsu after the surgery. When I arrived it was a surprise to learn she was in the ICU in an unstable condition. As I was looking into the rooms to find her I wondered what had happened.

When I found the appropriate room I didn't recognize Susan. The figure lying there looked like the Pillsbury Doughboy. The features were so barely discernable it was difficult to tell whether this was a man or a woman. Her daughter was with her. She told me Susan's spleen was punctured during surgery and it had to be removed. She lost a lot of blood and almost died. She was still in an unstable and critical condition.

I began doing opposite fingers and toes. There was a white film over Susan's eyes, and the first thing that started happening was the film started to shed from her eyes. Very soon after that Susan opened her eyes and looked at me. She told me how glad she was I was there. She was in and out of consciousness in the beginning of the treatment. As I continued, her features began to emerge and fill out. It was amazing to see, almost as if she was so close to death and then as she got closer to life she started taking form again. It seemed like she was coming back into her life.

By the end of the treatment Susan was fully awake. She asked if I could call Nordstrom's to tell them she would pick up her jacket in a few days! She is still alive one-and-a-half years later.

+×+ +×+ +×+

Jill continues her stories:

A nun who had liver cancer and was given a three month prognosis came to me for Jin Shin Jyutsu. Initially she was very thin and weak. She often talked about the doctor's prognosis. She said it was in the back of her mind like a hex and she couldn't shake it. As our Jin Shin Jyutsu treatments began and continued, she grew stronger, and with this renewed energy she became passionate about life again.

She went on to lead prayer groups; she started writing poetry. She would often bring her poems to our sessions and read the poetry to me. She pursued her Master's Degree in Psychology, which had been a life-long dream. Mary died four-and-a-half years after I met her. She told me it was the best four-and-a-half years of her life.

+×+ +×+ +×+

Jill's final story is about her grandmother.

When I arrived at the hospital my grandmother was in a coma and on life support machines. She had fallen down some steps and hit her head, causing a massive brain hemorrhage. The machines indicated she was brain dead.

I walked to her bed and spoke to her. Her eyes fluttered, she knew I was there. I began treating her. At first her pulses were quite irregular, then after a short while they became very smooth and peaceful. My grandmother was on life support systems and my mother was upset about pulling the plug. The nurses wanted to medicate my grandmother so that when the support systems were turned off she would not have a breathing struggle.

It was decision time. The plug was pulled, and instead of using medication, I continued treating my grandmother with Jin Shin Jyutsu. I did the #13 flow, the #3 flow,[3] I held the high #19s, the opposite fingers and toes, I crossed my hands and held the big toes. I wasn't able to reach her #4s. My grandmother died at 3:00 P.M. There was no struggle. She was very peaceful.

꘏ ꘏ ꘏

Gil Burmeister, Mary's husband and David's father, suffered a stroke shortly before Christmas, 1995. David shares his story with us.

At that time my father was 75 years old. After the stroke he went back and forth between rehabilitation and the hospital, attending to various medical projects that arose after the stroke. These included a blood clot in his lung, pneumonia, and sleep apnea, which led to a tracheotomy. I believe it was the sleep apnea that ultimately did him in. He was waking up dozens of times per night, which denied him the sleep vital to his healing. Each time my father was returned from the hospital unit to the rehabilitation unit, his doctor would comment that he had dodged yet another bullet.

Throughout the two months he was hospitalized I would visit and give him JSJ flows, oftentimes giving him

---

3. The #13 flow and the #3 flow are taught in the Jin Shin Jyutsu 5-Day Classes.

the spleen flow and the SEL #10 flow to help him with his energy level and breathing projects. Time and time again, we would see him improve and then have other complications that would compromise his health.

Finally, on Sunday evening, February 25, 1996, I felt my father had finally turned the corner and was now out of jeopardy. For the first time in months his pulses were balanced and his skin and eyes had become clear and bright. He could not speak due to the tracheotomy, but was very happy and relaxed. He wrote me a few short notes of love and thanks. For the first time since my father had become ill, I felt at ease. I ended my visit with the spleen and #10 flows, and said I'd see him the following morning. The next morning, before I was able to leave home, the hospital called to tell me my father had just died. I went to the hospital right away. The doctor said it was one of the most peaceful passings he could imagine. He had been on morning rounds and was with my father when he died. He said my father had drifted into a dreamlike state, and went into respiratory arrest.

I now believe that what I experienced the evening before, the calm and balanced pulses, was my father being fully balanced and in harmony for making his transition.

❦ ❦ ❦

Many of the stories in this book end with peaceful passings, but it is important to be clear here. The time preceding death can be painful, complicated medically, and terrifying for the patient; and it can be emotionally and physically draining for the caregivers, no matter how much one may love the patient. This time is rarely easy.

A Touching Good-Bye

Betsie Haar, a member of the Advisory Council for Jin Shin Jyutsu, Inc., and a long-time practitioner of this Art, shares with us the story of her beloved father-in-law. He struggled with a myriad of medical issues, and though Jin Shin Jyutsu helped some of his problems, it could not prevent his death. Even so, Betsie describes the blessing Jin Shin Jyutsu is for both the giver and the receiver.

When my beloved father-in-law, age 83, went into the hospital to be treated for an infected toe we were concerned but not alarmed. But as with so many older people not in good health, it turned out that this was the beginning of a cascade of medical problems that would result in his death several weeks later.

Dad was receiving aggressive treatment for his infection at one of the best hospitals in the world, but he was unhappy about being in the hospital and he had a lot of arthritic pain in his spine, hips, and shoulders. He was not the most compliant of patients and became depressed and a little cranky, didn't want to exercise, and lost his appetite. He just wanted to stay in bed and grumbled at people not to bother him. Mom could get him to eat only a little bit, mostly meat with gravy and a few potatoes. He became constipated. Perhaps all this contributed to his developing an intestinal obstruction, but whatever the cause, he was now in more trouble.

My sister-in-law lived near the hospital and was visiting Dad every day with Mom. She's a physical therapist and was eager to try Jin Shin Jyutsu with Dad even though she had never studied it. Over the phone I suggested she sit at the end of the bed, cross her arms and hold Dad's calves with each hand: right hand fully contacting the right calf, left hand on left calf. We call this "palming the calves"[4] and it's great for burns, skin ailments, and the intestines. It can be a bit awkward to do so you have to make sure you're comfortable, but it's really worth it.

After 15 or 20 minutes of this, Dad's intestines began to rumble and he was able to pass gas. My sister-in-law was amazed and delighted, this meant there wasn't a complete obstruction. But as Dad was in poor health the decision was made to operate and he went into surgery.

He came out of surgery exhausted and frightened by the respirator that was still inserted. He was in some degree of congestive heart failure and was having difficulty breathing on his own, and required sedation to keep him from trying to remove the respirator. But too much sedation would be harmful to his various organ systems that were now struggling. In addition he was being fed through a nasal gastric tube that had to stay in until he could move his bowels. He couldn't talk with all the apparatus in his throat but his eyes were very expressive and told the story of his distress. My husband held Dad's hand and spoke with him quietly and comforted him. I took a turn at palming Dad's calves, and I guess was able to encourage his intestines with this gentle art of Jin Shin Jyutsu because he was soon able to move his bowels. We were thrilled with this development because that meant the nasal gastric tube, which had caused him so much discomfort, could be removed.

I wish I could say that after the nasal gastric tube was removed his heart was able to recover as well, but it wasn't

---

4. "Palming the calves" is described in Chapter 8.

to be, and Dad passed away a few days later. The whole family was there and Mom sat by his side till the end and told him stories of their life together, remembering deep into their childhood when she was in the Brownie Scouts with Dad's little sister.

I think loving touch is the most important thing we can do when our loved ones are ill. It's so important that the touch be non-invasive and gentle. It's a way of really being with someone, being fully present to someone regardless of his condition, without trying to fix him. It's the single most comforting thing we can do for someone who is suffering, and it eases our suffering as well. What is it about the Art of Jin Shin Jyutsu that encourages this? It seems to be built in.

Applying the Art in this loving and gentle way simply jump-starts and then helps to harmonize a person's own energetic rhythms of life so that harmony of mind, body and spirit is experienced. Over the years when I've shared Jin Shin Jyutsu with clients, relatives, and friends who are at the end of life it has seemed almost miraculous in calming their fears and bringing them reassurance and peace of mind. Isn't it the most natural and loving act — to help your loved one die peacefully?

In my family, all the older generation is now gone. I am profoundly grateful that I was able to let them know how much I cared by giving my loving touch to them in the days as they were passing away.

❀ ❀ ❀

4

Hearing the Need

Donna is a respiratory therapist in the intensive care unit of a hospital in New Orleans. I asked her about her experiences with people who were dying and what she considered to be their biggest needs. She thinks most people, if not afraid, are at least apprehensive. They want:

1. To be affirmed at this difficult time; to be acknowledged.
2. To be touched; to have a physical human contact.
3. Not to be alone.

A friend and colleague of Donna's who was a nurse at the hospital believed strongly in "being there" for his dying patients. If friends or loved ones were not present at the time of death, he was always there, holding the patient's hand. "I never let one of my patients die alone," he vowed. Later, when he died of cancer, Donna was there for him, holding his hand.

Many of the people who practice the Art of Jin Shin Jyutsu eventually become quite intuitive. Intuition, if we become attuned to listening, can be a source of wisdom. Here Mitzi "hears" the need of a mother.

In 1997, a young man asked if I would do Jin Shin Jyutsu with his ailing mother. He was working at a wellness center where I was practicing Jin Shin Jyutsu and he had received many sessions himself. His mother had been on kidney dialysis from a young age and now, a tiny woman in her early 50s, she was suffering the ill consequences of the procedures. Her skin appeared to be like leather. Nonetheless, she remained optimistic.

She was an amazing little woman. She had had years of medical "projects," yet she never complained. She would only comment if something felt better. As our Jin Shin Jyutsu sessions progressed I could sense her body responding in little ways. She often felt relief from headaches, or from the pain in her hips and knees resulting from the many joint replacements she had endured.

After treating her for some time, I left for a vacation. When I returned she was in the hospital, and I was called to go see her. There had been so many dramatic medical emergencies during her lifetime this one did not particularly alarm her family. I felt, though, this would probably be her last hospital visit.

The incision from her sternum to her pubic bone was not healing properly after an exploratory surgery. Still the family did not seem to be aware of the severity of the situation. Accepting of her imminent death, I sat by her right side. With my left hand I held her right palm, and with my right hand I held each of the fingers of her right hand one at a time. While holding her hand and fingers I recited the

Twenty-third Psalm. I felt a familiar vibrating energy passing through me. God was surely present. I felt a rush of dancing white lights all around us. I said to her, "Do not be afraid, God is waiting for you." I realized again this was not about saving her. All of the Jin Shin Jyutsu sessions she received allowed for the emergence of harmony and acceptance.

I said I would contact her son, who at that point had not yet said his good-byes. When I spoke to him I suggested he write down everything he ever wanted to tell his mother, and go to be with her as soon as possible. He called me the next day. He had written a letter of love and thanks, brought it to the hospital and read it to her. As soon as he finished, his mother passed away.

※※※

Some expressions of need are subtle, and others can be quite direct. Bill heard a more urgent plea from his friend, Frank.

When my friend, Frank, was diagnosed with cancer of the bladder, the bladder was removed and the prognosis was good. One-and-a-half years later, when Frank complained of abdominal pain, the doctors didn't find anything alarming, so Frank and I went to San Antonio for a Jin Shin Jyutsu class enroute to a month's holiday at Laguna Beach, CA. God works in mysterious ways, because it was during this class I wrote in my notes that Wayne Hackett said to hold Safety Energy Lock #4 and #16 in order to help someone "exit" at the time of death. Neither of us realized how close that was for Frank.

On the drive to Laguna Beach Frank began experiencing horrible pain, which continued when we arrived there. Even though I was a relative newcomer to Jin Shin Jyutsu, I gave Frank sessions daily, which did help the pain to a degree and allowed Frank to sleep. When the doctors there could find no cause, but the pain continued, we returned to Ft. Worth.

At this point the doctors found that cancer had spread throughout his abdomen and liver, and recommended chemotherapy and radiation, without which they did not think he would survive three weeks. Frank was agitated after his first chemotherapy treatment. I did the Jin Shin Jyutsu 3rd Method of Correction,[1] which seemed to help. I continued giving these sessions throughout the chemotherapy and into the radiation therapy, but after the 20th of 30 radiation treatments he couldn't tolerate being touched, even on his toes. After that I didn't do any more Jin Shin Jyutsu on him.

Frank survived for three months. Whether in the hospital or at home, he needed no pain pills. Then one day, he must have known he was close to dying. He wanted to go back to the hospital. Though he was not in pain, he was immediately put on morphine. I think he would have died that night without the morphine, which put him mostly out of his mind. But now he continued to linger, in a desperate state. After ten days we moved him to a smaller hospital near my home in Mineral Wells, Texas.

Between morphine doses Frank pleaded, "Please get me out of here." I gently slid my right hand behind his head and held his left #4. My left hand went to his left outer ankle, #16. When I connected those two safety energy locks,

---

1. The 3rd Method of Correction is taught in the Jin Shin Jyutsu 5-Day Class.

I immediately felt the Spirit leave the feet and go right out through the top of the body. Woosh! That fast. He was gone.

I knew he was gone. I had literally felt it happening. The reason I think I was given that beautiful opportunity with death was to teach me our Spirit goes to a better place. I had always wondered. I needed to be shown. The energy in your body is your Spirit. The body dies, we leave behind this shell, the body. The Spirit never dies; it goes on.

Curiously, when I recounted this story to Wayne Hackett, my Jin Shin Jyutsu instructor, he said he had never said to use the #4 and #16 at the time of death. It was amazing. I had heard his voice say it and had put it in my notes. I really do believe we "hear" what we need to hear, and when the time came this was the exactly right combination to help Frank's Spirit take flight.

༂༂༂

A Touching Good-Bye

Carlos Gutterres, a Jin Shin Jyutsu instructor with a practice in Brazil, was asked to go to the hospital to help a man in the final stages of cancer. Carlos learned an important lesson during this process, from which we can all benefit.

> He was 40 years old, his bladder had stopped and all of his organs were in collapse. The doctors wanted him to be unconscious because of the pain. They gave him two days to live.
>
> It was difficult for me to give him treatments because of all of the tubes and hospital paraphernalia, so for two days I did opposite fingers and toes twice a day. On the third day the family was called in. Although he remained unconscious, all of his bodily functions had returned. The family was encouraged and wanted me to continue working with him. As I began the Jin Shin Jyutsu fingers and toes treatment, this unconscious man took my hands off of his body. After he did this for the fourth time I finally understood. He did not want treatments. Even completely unconscious he was able to remove my hands four times. Shortly after that he died.

⌁ ⌁ ⌁

Carlos finally heard the need of this unconscious man. There are other cases of people in comas, even those supposedly paralyzed, who find the strength to communicate, either by raising an arm or leg, or squeezing a hand, that they have had enough Jin Shin Jyutsu. Never assume a person in a coma is completely unaware of what is happening around him or her. Even infants and young children, whether healthy or ill, intuitively know when they have had enough, and communicate this by wiggling or pushing away the Jin Shin Jyutsu hands.

Any of us who understand the potential positive effects of Jin Shin Jyutsu suffer the problem of wanting to proselytize. We have clearly seen and experienced the benefits it affords, and we want to pass it on. We are always saddened when someone refuses, feeling an opportunity lost. It is crucial for us to understand there are those who, for whatever reason, are not interested in experiencing Jin Shin Jyutsu. It is important as one way of "hearing the need" to honor that decision, and to refrain from being insistent.

We would all like to be attuned to the one we are helping. Giving Jin Shin Jyutsu to another allows the giver to slow down, find peace, and hear more clearly the need, however it is presented. Also remember, whether another wants the Jin Shin Jyutsu or not, you can always benefit from doing it to yourself.

5

LIVING WITH QUALITY

With a painful illness or a devastating prognosis how do you continue to live with a sense of quality in life? How do you retain a sense of control over your life once you begin the monumental task of coping with hospitals and clinics and your treatments and the confusion of so many bills? How do you maintain a sense of dignity with all of the indignities you have to suffer? Alicia Heard sat at my kitchen table and talked about Mac's illness and death. Her heartfelt remembrance helps to answer these questions.

It was Christmas, 1999, and I was trying to think of a present for my husband, Mac. He had recently published his book *French Quarter Manual, An Architectural Guide to New Orleans' Vieux Carre.* Besides giving his regular architectural classes at Tulane University, he was inundated with requests for book signings and lectures about the French Quarter. In spite of all this success, I felt there was something different about him, he seemed to be getting upset easily and he was tense, almost harried. I had enjoyed my Jin Shin Jyutsu sessions with Marcia, and felt it would be nice for Mac to have them. He could come to Marcia's beautiful place, be quiet, and collect himself. I gave him a present of three Jin Shin Jyutsu sessions for Christmas. In retrospect, of course, I realize it was the illness of which we were unaware that was making him so tense.

He enjoyed the three sessions, and Mac and I laughed on Valentine's Day when we surprised each other with the gift of three more Jin Shin Jyutsu sessions. About this time he began complaining about a pain in his neck and shoulder. Since this is a symptom we all have from time to time, it didn't seem too unusual.

In May, despite a virus he found quite depleting, we left on a long anticipated return trip to Rome. Our second day there Mac felt considerably worse, and thinking it was the shingles, had medicine Fed-Ex'd to Rome. It, of course, had no effect. Though he didn't feel well, we stayed for our three weeks, with Mac resting most of the day, then enjoying late afternoon strolls and dinners at night. We saw and did a lot actually, and it amazes me how he could approach Rome with so much enthusiasm, knowing now how sick he was.

The day after we returned to New Orleans we began what would become a round of seeing many doctors. Mac was diagnosed with kidney cancer that had metastasized to the cervical area of the spine. At the end of June and early July he had surgery on his neck, followed a week later with the removal of his kidney. Two weeks later the pain had returned to the neck and arm. The tumor was continuing to grow; radiation was advised.

Though Mac and I recognized the seriousness of his illness, we both thought he had maybe five years to live. We thought we had more time together than we actually did. Mac continued teaching his classes at Tulane's School of Architecture that fall. He was filled with interest in everything around him. He planned many projects, had several books mapped out. He took time with our children individually and was very dear to me. He seemed to understand what was important. He was obviously relishing life. He began having Jin Shin Jyutsu sessions three times a week.

By the beginning of 2001 it was more and more difficult for Mac to feel well, but he never dwelled on his illness. Each day he got up, dressed, and had a plan for the day. He kept himself and all of us going with his interest and enthusiasm. Jin Shin Jyutsu was very much a part of the pattern of his life. He told me how pleasant and lovely it was to go to Marcia's house for the sessions. The gentleness and quietness of it must have helped him maintain his calm and his sense of self. When it got to the point he could only have one outing a day, the Jin Shin Jyutsu session was his choice.

You know, he never felt sorry for himself, he never said, "Why me?" He felt great compassion for other people, he saw himself as one of many who were ill. He maintained to the very end a great personal dignity and a sense of humor. He could always rally to preside over his place at the dinner table, even when sitting in his wheelchair and barely able to eat.

By the end of March we set Mac's bed in the dining room. It was the center of the house, basically, so he could be aware of all the comings and goings. I remember what a beautiful spring it was, and we opened the windows onto the garden and the door onto the back gallery. I felt a spiritual quality about the weather, with windows open and a constant breeze blowing off the Mississippi River, with the dancing light and shadows, the birds singing. There were fresh flowers blooming in the yard and each day I could pick something different to put on the mantelpiece. I remember those weeks of people coming to the house, a steady stream of visitors, friends bringing greatly appreciated meals, and those wanting to have a final visit with Mac. A Hospice worker came twice a week to check on him, and a home health nurse came twice a week to bathe him and tend to his needs. They were helpful, but with a busy workload they didn't have a chance to linger and just "be there."

So it was particularly helpful to have Marcia come once a day and give Mac Jin Shin Jyutsu sessions for an hour. It was a gift really, to the whole family. It was so nice to be able to say, "Marcia's here to do Jin Shin Jyutsu with Mac. This is a quiet time in the house." Everyone cooperated and it became very still. It was that way when the minister came, too, but he wasn't there as often. With Marcia coming, we could count on a quiet time every day.

The children and I felt that Marcia had a truly appropriate gift. She taught the family that gift so that we, in turn, could give it to Mac and feel we, too, were helping him. It was different from the dear friends who brought food, conversation, caring, which were wonderful, but at the same time, demanded a response from us. We had to keep reassuring them they were doing the right thing, they were being helpful. Somehow Marcia just knew Jin Shin Jyutsu was the most appropriate thing in the world, and it was. It provided peace and calmness. It was just the right thing. It was what we all needed. I know food is an expression of love and caring, and is much appreciated, so it is hard for me to explain the difference. The Jin Shin Jyutsu brought to all of us a quietness, and a peacefulness and a sense of release. Mac would look forward to Marcia's coming. He wouldn't hesitate to tell anyone else visiting when she arrived that it was time for them to leave, that this was a special time. Wouldn't it be nice if our whole society had this gift to give one another?

The medication and illness made him agitated, and the steady stream of visitors may have added to that. But during a Jin Shin Jyutsu session he would always calm down and lose the agitation, and remain calm for a long time afterwards. We appreciated the short list of simple Jin Shin Jyutsu methods Marcia gave and explained to us. The children and I did these to Mac when we sat with him and could see the difference it made in his comfort.

On one particular afternoon our children and I thought Mac was going. Wendell, Lucy and I were there with him. The light and the quality of the air coming into the room were beautiful. As we sat quietly with Mac I had the feeling of a ship in the Mississippi River, a block away. In my mind I saw a beautiful old wooden ship with an arched prow, like a Viking ship, with towering sails. The people on the ship, anonymous, wearing simple robes, had come to get Mac. They were waiting for him. Out in the garden I could sense the light of the ship and the beautiful lines of sails coming into the garden in waves, in the river, in the garden, and all around us. It was beautiful and wonderful and serene.

Mac did not die that day. He awakened, saw us all sitting there, and said, "Well!" His life had been so filled with activity, with projects, with responsibility, I think he didn't know how to shut down and let go. At times I would sense him "going off" and being somewhere else, but he was not happy there, he was not ready to give up this life. Marcia felt those same happenings on several occasions when they were together with Jin Shin Jyutsu.

On April 6, while taking a walk, I tripped and broke my right wrist. The operation to set it was April 9. One of my funniest (now!) memories is of me lying in the bed with my cast enveloped arm in some contraption that held it over my head, and Mac being wheeled into the room and asking, "What is the modus operandi for the day?" When he realized there could no longer be plans for every day, because he was beyond that, and, at this particular point, so was I, he knew he did not want to go on. I, and each of the children, went to him separately to tell him it was all right to go, that we would each be capable of managing our lives.

As an accomplished pianist, Mac had enjoyed music throughout his life, so it was no surprise when he began, in his last few days, to hear beautiful music. He said it was new music that he had never heard before. Several times he said to people who visited, "We'll all meet again by the river." These were ancient words from deep within his southern roots. He had never used this terminology before, so we felt he was slowly beginning to go somewhere else. He was enchanted by a documentary on television one night that had to do with the south. It brought back so much of his childhood and the people and voices he had known.

Finally the Hospice worker told us we needed to allow Mac to have morphine because of his extreme pain. We had resisted this earlier because being clear headed was so important to him. Now we agreed, and as we had feared, the morphine made him quite agitated. It was Easter weekend and Marcia was away with her family, so we began doing Jin Shin Jyutsu ourselves. When Mac became agitated we would do what Marcia had taught us, and he would calm down, even when full of morphine. Jin Shin Jyutsu is extraordinarily helpful. Even with my broken wrist up in the air, I could put my other hand on the back of his neck, or hold his fingers, or his feet, and in this way really communicate with him and feel that what I was doing meant something to him. He couldn't tolerate being hugged or rubbed in any way. This is so gentle, it calmed him, quieted his breath. It also calmed anyone else in the room or in the house. It had many, many positive effects. Somehow Jin Shin Jyutsu frees your mind, allowing you to go into other places. It induces a meditative state, calming the mind and the body, freeing your imagination. It is a pleasant place between wakefulness and sleep.

Mac died on April 14, the day before Easter. It was a beautiful morning, very quiet. I freshened Mac, who was sleeping well after a night when he had had difficulty breathing. I sat quietly with him, putting my hand under his head, saying the Jesus prayer, "Jesus Christ, Son of God, have mercy upon us," as a mantra. I held his fingers. After about 45 minutes I could tell his breath was going, so I called our son Wendell inside, and telephoned our daughter to come. As I had my hand on the back of his neck Mac simply breathed his last breath. It was very quiet, painless. I felt his spirit going. Just then Lucy arrived and leaned her face close to his. "Lucy's here," I said. He smiled.

꒷꒦꒷꒦꒷

A Touching Good-Bye

Waltraud Riegger-Krause, a Jin Shin Jyutsu instructor and practitioner who lives in Germany, helped another person who seemed determined to maintain quality in his life.

A man in his 30s began coming to me for Jin Shin Jyutsu sessions. I knew, from the person who had recommended him to me, that he was HIV positive, though he did not give any label as his reason for coming. He was a strong and healthy looking young man and always arrived on his bicycle. It was strange working with him, knowing he was HIV positive, but with him never mentioning it. I respected his privacy and did not ask for any reasons for his wanting Jin Shin Jyutsu sessions. I believe people deserve their privacy, he could decide for himself whether or when to tell me.

He came regularly once a week for four or five years. I normally work on someone by listening to the Jin Shin Jyutsu pulses and using the flows that are indicated at that time. I also did the #3 flow often, to strengthen the immune system. During the time he came to me for sessions I also taught him self-help he could do when he was at home. I suggested: holding SEL #3 and each finger one by one; holding his ring fingers; and holding SELs #11 and #25, and #11 and #15. I also taught him how to do the 36 Breaths. Occasionally he would miss a session. He would explain to me he was in the hospital with a lung problem or something else, but he never told me his label and I did not ask.

It eventually became obvious he was getting weaker. For instance, he no longer rode his bicycle to the sessions. I continued doing the Jin Shin Jyutsu flows that his pulses indicated would be most useful. Often that was the Lung flow to help his breathing, or the Large Intestine flow because of problems with his anus.

He must have felt the Jin Shin Jyutsu was beneficial to him because he continued to come, even when getting up the steps to my second floor office became difficult. At one point a nurse came for treatments for a sprained ankle. She was one of the people caring for him and he had told her I might be able to help her ankle. She said to me, "What you are doing must be a very good thing, because I have much experience doing home care for HIV patients. I think he would already have been dead without these treatments. Also, his quality of life is so much better than other patients I see. He has a good spirit. He is more up, he is not so depressed."

Then one of his friends began coming for treatments. Though the nurse had mentioned HIV, neither he nor his friend ever mentioned it. I continued to respect their silence, not wanting to infringe on their privacy.

When he became so weak he was no longer able to come to my office, he asked if I would come to his home, which I did. He had lung problems, and the Jin Shin Jyutsu did help to clear his breathing. I did the #3 flow often, to help the immune system, lungs, respiratory, and breathing. This opens the shoulders and helps breathing. When breathing is in harmony, the whole being is in harmony. He had, from the beginning of our sessions together, been interested in the philosophy of this Art of Jin Shin Jyutsu and enjoyed talking about it with me. Money was not a problem for him, so all of this time he had also been receiving the best medical treatment available.

Working on him at home, while his body got weaker, I could see his eyes becoming clearer. I felt this expressed his spirit and awareness. His body was consumed with the illness, but not his spirit. I always felt he came for Jin Shin Jyutsu treatments for all those years because it nourished his soul. He seemed to become more and more at peace with himself, more able to accept and deal with his illness and his entire life situation. As a practitioner you can sense what "state" a person is in, whether he or she is tense, very restless, is consumed with thoughts, is caught in attitudes. In the same way you can feel a person's peace and calmness.

The weaker he became, the more his stillness and peace became obvious, and the clearer the eyes became. Our sessions were like meditations. I felt the presence of a spiritual atmosphere growing around him the weaker he became. Rarely was there much talk of any of these things. Often there was silence for the entire session. I experienced this stillness and peace also, a feeling of Oneness, just Being One with that person. It was a wonderful experience, and I felt he was in this same state, so very much at Peace.

Finally he was taken to the hospital. I only visited him there once, then a few days later he died.

Looking back, I think Jin Shin Jyutsu helped him in several ways. It helped him physically and with pain; it helped him emotionally to deal with his whole situation; and it helped him spiritually in that he was able to die consciously and peacefully. I am grateful to have known and worked with him.

A Touching Good-Bye

After Carlos had been practicing Jin Shin Jyutsu in Brazil for one year a friend brought his mother in for a Jin Shin Jyutsu session.

She was desperate. During surgery for kidney cancer it was discovered the cancer had spread to her liver and lung. Her doctor told her she had six months to live. She confided to me she was the strong person in her family of brothers, sisters and children. She was the main caregiver and felt they needed her.

I told her I could not promise miracles, but what Jin Shin Jyutsu could do was enhance her quality of life while she lived. She came for 21 straight days of treatments. During those 21 days she changed. She became more confident, full of energy, full of life. She even went to her dentist to have her upper plate remade. The dentist wondered, "Why are you doing this?"

After the 21 days of treatments she continued Jin Shin Jyutsu treatments twice weekly. She went to swimming class. She continued supporting and problem solving for all of her family. Then she stopped the sessions. She felt well and she was busy.

Eight months after she stopped the Jin Shin Jyutsu treatments she went to the hospital for an examination. The doctor discovered the cancer had spread. She lived one week. She called me. She was in pain and did not want to take strong medications because she wanted to be alert to see her last son when he arrived. In the hospital I held #16 and #5 on each ankle. After a while she was able to sleep for an hour without pain. Her last son arrived and she was able to talk with him. Afterwards she took the pain medication, and four hours later she died.

I was grateful for the Jin Shin Jyutsu she had received. After her diagnosis she had been able to live a normal life, full of motivation, and without fear of pain. And when the end came it was quick and without suffering.

❖ ❖ ❖

Jin Shin Jyutsu does not offer an escape from death. Those who do choose to make use of it often find either peace, calmness, reduced pain and agitation, deeper sleep, renewed energy, or all of the above. What do you have to lose by trying it?

6

GRIEVING

Grief is an individual and extremely personal reaction to traumatic situations in our lives. We grieve about many things, death being one of the most obvious. We are each affected differently, depending on our particular situation. For many, the grieving process begins with a diagnosis and lasts until and beyond death. For some a death has been unexpected, so we are unprepared. Maybe the death of a loved one has been untimely, as in being predeceased by a child or young adult.

Most of us have a wistful picture in our heads of living to a ripe old age and dying peacefully in our sleep, surrounded by family and friends. This is exactly what happened in the following story of Betsy Matteson's mother, Elizabeth. And yet, for Ann Bardwell, in the second story, her husband's illness at a relatively young age was a shock neither of them had anticipated. Whatever the circumstances, the stories in this book make clear Jin Shin Jyutsu helps to ease this painful

process. Breast cancer is genetic in Betsy Matteson's family.
Here she graces us with her mother's story.

My great-grandmother, grandmother, aunt and mother
all developed cancer and died with this label.[1] My mother,
Elizabeth, who had seen both her mother and younger
sister precede her in death, had always assumed this would
be her way also. She did not tell anyone she was ill until,
in 1998, at the age of 86, she was diagnosed with Stage IV
breast cancer.

"What do you want to do about it?" I asked when she
called me over to tell me. I think because she had seen
other family members have surgery and chemotherapy and
radiation to no avail, she did not believe there was any way
to cure it, and did not want any type of treatment. At this
time she didn't even have a doctor. I did convince her that
we needed to find an M.D. who would support her just in
case there was a time when she might need some palliative
care. It is, after all, a bit tricky to pick a name out of the
yellow pages, call up and say, "Hi. I'm dying and need some
help," and expect them to leap to your aid.

We were fortunate to find a doctor who understood
the situation and was comfortable with letting the illness
take its course, and who supported her decision to die at

---

1. Within each of us an underlying harmony is always present, even when
we experience some disharmony or illness. These disharmonies all arise
from the same cause, blockage of life energy. In Jin Shin Jyutsu these
disharmonies are referred to as labels. Big scary labels such as heart disease
or cancer indicate a lot of stuck energy. Less scary labels like indigestion
or colds indicate lesser blockages. All disharmonies benefit from the
clearing of blocked energy.

home with Hospice. At that time it was thought she had six months to live.

I am a Jin Shin Jyutsu practitioner, as are many of my friends, and my mother had received treatments prior to her illness and was familiar with this Art, so it was a natural thought to turn there for help. In 1998 I had just recently finished my third 5-Day Class and I felt somewhat out of my "comfort zone," so I gave my mother daily sessions and she also received weekly sessions with Philomena. During this period her attitude was very hopeful for a remission, and she was able to live as she always had, independently and on her own terms.

The wished-for remission was not to be, and the cancer progressed into her spine. She then had a weekend bout of extreme back pain that put her into the hospital for the only time in her illness. She was given methadone for pain and decided to try radiation, not for the cancer, but to reduce the swelling in her spine so she could be relatively pain free until the end. She was scheduled for ten sessions and was told not to expect any unpleasant side effects except tiredness. She had two sessions, both of which made her quite ill. She stopped the radiation. When we brought her home it was in a wheelchair and she was unable to walk again. She decided to stop the methadone because it bothered her stomach, and miraculously she had no more significant pain.

The next few weeks were filled with visits from friends, calls and letters, a gathering of family. My mother was bed-ridden and everyone wanted to see her. The outpouring of love was astonishing. During this time her stomach bothered her most and we did fingers and toes, stomach flow, held her #4s and #7s. It took only a small amount of Jin Shin Jyutsu to relieve her discomfort.

During the last week of her life she was no longer able to eat or drink, and holding her #4s was the extent of her Jin Shin Jyutsu. We think she may have had a small stroke because for the last three days she was unable to communicate with us. I continued to hold her #4s and realized her left #4 was "pulseless," while her right #4 was "pulsing." It made me think perhaps she was ready to go before her body was. My mother died peacefully, with no mental or emotional distress and very little physical discomfort. Surrounded by those who loved her, she was blessed with God's Grace, and I was still holding her #4s.

In many ways events after my mother's death were as astonishing as those that came before. It was a warm August night but well after dark. Inside we were drinking a toast and listening to music, but a friend outside the house told us there was a golden light streaming out of the windows. Mary Jane, a friend who had given Elizabeth Jin Shin Jyutsu treatments, woke in the night, from midnight until 3:00 A.M., which was the time period when all this transpired. Another friend, on vacation in Austria, broke into tears at dinner because she knew "Elizabeth has died." Another friend came early the next morning because she felt "something had happened." At 2:00 A.M. I was outside watching very unusual cloud formations stream by at a rapid rate but with a lot of moonlight. I am not Catholic, but was told later this was the day for the Feast of Transfiguration. I don't know if that is correct but I find it most interesting.

After the services were finished and life had some calmness again, I received Jin Shin Jyutsu every day for a week from my friend, Mary Jane. I knew the 2nd Method of Correction was a part of most of my sessions. I was never as grief stricken with my mother's death as I had been with my father's many years before. When he died of a heart attack at age 64 it had been a total shock and a completely difference experience. Perhaps being with someone and witnessing the decline adds to the acceptance, but I know Jin Shin Jyutsu smoothed the process for Mother and for me. All these combined to make it a less painful loss.

The opportunity to be with someone when he or she dies doesn't come to all of us. Caring for my mother was the hardest and the most rewarding experience of my life to date. For a brief period I knew what it is to truly live in the NOW.

I think the experience of grief deepens our compassion. It makes us realize we are more caring than we know. My concept of Jin Shin Jyutsu changed dramatically during this process. We must give and receive in equal amounts. I try now never to schedule "too tightly," so I have time for my clients. Their ability to pay is a minor consideration. My treating has become more intuitive and I have greater confidence in my intuition. It occurs to me that I will probably never memorize any flow from start to finish or know what page it's on in the Jin Shin Jyutsu text, and it's not important. It is important that through Jin Shin Jyutsu we connect with one another.

꒰꒱꒰꒱

A Touching Good-Bye

Ann Bardwell's husband, Alan, unfortunately died at a much younger age than Elizabeth. How does one reconcile a loved one dying in the prime of life? How does one cope with devastating news? Possibly one way of transforming loss is by making it meaningful, finding some positive way of using the experience. Ann Bardwell's exquisite story is her gift to all of us.

Alan was an avid fly-fisherman, and some of the most treasured times of our courtship were spent on the Frying Pan and Roaring Fork Rivers near Aspen, where he taught me to fish. I came to love our trips to the river together. In the early years of our marriage it was more about being on an adventure with Alan. But later, after I had learned more about fishing, I began to feel some envy when he went off with his buddies for their annual pilgrimage to the Big Horn River in Montana, famous for its fly-fishing. They had gone on their yearly river voyage for the last 15 years and there was no question that it was a "men only" trip. But this year I felt a longing to experience this place that Alan loved and he was inspired to share it with me.

We didn't cancel our plans after Alan discovered a lump under his arm. The biopsy would come after our fishing trip. It was magical on the Big Horn and the rainbow trout were plentiful. We stayed in a campsite at Ft. Smith, in a small trailer right near the river. Before we left on our trip a friend in Boulder, who had taken a Jin Shin Jyutsu Self-Help Class, taught us how to do a very basic Jin Shin Jyutsu hold. I can't remember now exactly what it was, maybe placing one hand over the other under the armpit. I do remember how unnatural it seemed to us at that time. We laughed at the oddity of it. We had no real sense of how it would be helpful. I look back at that beginning in contrast to the total blessing Jin Shin Jyutsu soon became for us. On that first time, in the little trailer near the Big Horn River, though, in our halting and unnatural first efforts at Jin Shin Jyutsu, Alan did comment that he liked being touched. It was also a time just to be quiet together and to settle.

In April 1991, Alan was diagnosed with melanoma that had metastasized. The original site was never determined. The surgeon told us that the tumor under his left armpit had probably been growing for several years. Five lymph nodes were involved. Later, the cancer spread to his lungs and liver. Alan died in August 1992.

After the diagnosis we wanted to find a way of working with his body to support him physically. I was also looking for a way that I could help myself physically. We decided to take Susan Brook's Jin Shin Jyutsu Self-Help Class. Arriving on that first day of class, Alan and I had absolutely no idea of the significance it would have in our lives. We began doing Jin Shin Jyutsu at that class and continued for the 16 months Alan lived. Susan also gave him treatments, and even after he became too tired and weak to do anything else, he would find the energy to climb the stairs to Susan's office. Twice we were able to go to Scottsdale for intensive weeks with Mary.

During Alan's illness Jin Shin Jyutsu gave both of us a sense of wellness and peace. It became our favorite way of being together. The use of Jin Shin Jyutsu gave both of us so much confidence. The confidence came from knowing there was something we could do, and knowing that what we did would actually be helpful. Alan always felt better after a session, and it eased my mind knowing there was something I could do that helped him. It always eased his pain.

Jin Shin Jyutsu was one of our major ways of being together. As his illness progressed we did hours of Jin Shin Jyutsu every day. While I was giving him treatments, Alan would fall asleep, or lie with his eyes closed. For a couple, this is one of the most profoundly intimate ways you can be together, especially when your spouse's body is going through such radical changes. On one of these occasions when he was quietly lying there, he opened his eyes and said softly, "These are some of the best times." The heartfelt tone in his voice touched me deeply. There were not many things in his life that felt as good to him and he was grateful and enjoying it. I didn't know at the time but was told later, that I was "receiving" Jin Shin Jyutsu at the same time that I was "giving" it, that I was very much a part of the Jin Shin Jyutsu loop.[2] I only knew I was having incredibly profound times with Alan.

We were married in 1988. For a wedding gift Alan's mother gave us a hand-crafted calligraphy. The framed quote was: "Come Grow Old with Me, the Best Is Yet to Be." At the time of our marriage we were 36 and 38. I understood the meaning of the quote to be about the richness of longevity in a marriage, but didn't really relate to it at that time and put it away in a drawer for safekeeping. At age 44 and now living with cancer, Alan was growing very old. He was thin and frail. With blond hair and blue eyes his natural, fair skin tone had changed to a dark blue-brown.

---

2. Many people find that giving Jin Shin Jyutsu quietly to another helps harmonize their own body, mind and spirit.

He was growing physically old and at the same time very wise. I came upon the calligraphy quote one day, which now had a totally different meaning because of how our life was unfolding. I was startled by how profoundly it spoke to the truth of our experience. As Alan moved toward his death I was able to accompany him. "The Best Is Yet to Be" foretold the sacred journey that completely unraveled the fabric of our life together and transformed us both. I can't imagine what it would have been like without Jin Shin Jyutsu.

You know, doing Jin Shin Jyutsu doesn't demand great strength or special skills. I had never attended a 5-Day Class and didn't understand it on a scientific or philosophical level. This ancient healing Art had so many aspects. For us it was totally pragmatic. It got the job done. At the same time it was a powerful way of being together that was intimate and fulfilling for me, even when Alan was asleep. The treatments became my practice for being focused and being present. As Alan grew thinner and darker, his face became exquisitely beautiful to me. The person he became was this gorgeous being. The caregiver of Jin Shin Jyutsu has the opportunity to be with the Truth of whatever is happening, and preparing for what's coming. Alan said to me he didn't like looking in the mirror, it frightened him. And there I was, looking at him for hours. In many ways the person who is the caregiver doesn't have the luxury of not looking. I guess he was looking at himself from the outside while I was seeing his spirit.

We had been on many fishing trips to the Roaring Fork and Frying Pan Rivers near Aspen, and what we recognized would be our last one was in July, 1992, five weeks before Alan died. At this point he was quite weak and sleeping most of the day. He slept in the car and also when we settled into our friend's house. We did Jin Shin Jyutsu when we arrived. I was concerned that the fishing trip would be too much for him, so I did hours of the Spleen Flow to give him energy. We fished the next day in the late afternoon and into the evening under a full moon. Our companions and protectors for this trip were the same friends he went to the Bighorn with. They all wanted to be with Alan for a last float down the Roaring Fork. It was exhausting for him, but also a triumph for both of us. Afterwards I continued holding the Spleen Flow. It helped Alan to regain energy and feel better. This is what I mean about Jin Shin Jyutsu being pragmatic. It gave us the right tools for the job. The results were palpable. I could see them and feel them.

Jin Shin Jyutsu provided a "container" for us during Alan's illness. Instead of running around, busily doing — avoiding death — you sit still and BE with whatever the experience is at that moment. Those hours of Jin Shin Jyutsu with Alan gave me a reservoir of memories and experiences of being present to him, of stillness and confidence. It was a helpful preparation for the journey of grief because I was in the practice of being with what is. Alan and I were practicing Buddhists, which helped me through all of this, to understand that the resolution of grief was less the point than the lessons of the journey.

A month after Alan's death I had an intensive week of Jin Shin Jyutsu with Mary in Scottsdale. In appreciation for what she had given us through the gift of Jin Shin Jyutsu I took her a beautiful blouse and wrote this card:

A Touching Good-Bye

Mary,

Please accept this small gift with love from Alan and me. The help you have given us through Jin Shin Jyutsu has been sacred to both of us.

During Alan's illness, Jin Shin gave both of us a feeling of well-being and peace. The time we spent each day doing Jin Shin was our favorite time and way of being together. It was precious to us.

Jin Shin gave us both so much confidence because it almost always helped Alan to feel better. It eased my mind tremendously knowing that there was always something I could do to help him.

You gave Alan great comfort, Mary. He had so much confidence in your healing and in the healing power of Jin Shin. I am certain that Jin Shin gave Alan more time to live and as a result gave us both more precious time to be with each other. Now that I am alone, I look back at all our times together doing Jin Shin and I know that we were truly blessed, both to have that time and to be with each other in a peaceful and loving way. It means everything to me that I can look back and know that I loved Alan my very best.

Jin Shin was a precious gift to both of us. Thank you for helping us and loving us.

With much love and gratitude,

Ann and Alan

Telling you this story is for honoring Alan. Jin Shin made a huge difference to him. I cannot think of anything better to do with someone living with a life threatening illness, or with someone knowing he or she is in the process of dying. I say this as much for what I experienced in my way of being as for the benefits Alan received. I was transformed through my journey with Alan.

✴✴✴

7

Transforming Souls

Earlier I suggested that people who know and value Jin Shin Jyutsu should take care not to be too insistent in forcing it on others. Of course, there is an exception to every rule, and Jin Shin Jyutsu instructor and practitioner, Jill Holden, demonstrates that exception here in Cynthia Broshi's account.

At age 20 months, with symptoms nearly critical, Cynthia's daughter, Lucy Lenssen, was diagnosed with cystic fibrosis, a label considered genetic, progressive, and incurable. Medical intervention saved Lucy's life and filled their days, but the prognosis was poor. Jill Holden, a friend of a friend, offered Lucy a series of Jin Shin Jyutsu sessions. Not understanding what this was, Cynthia only accepted after the third time Jill offered, so as not to appear rude. The results were immediate and profound. Jill was able to teach Cynthia flows to use daily on Lucy. Jin Shin Jyutsu became the only thing that enabled Lucy to feel good in her body.

Nine months later Cynthia began studying with Mary Burmeister and sharing Jin Shin Jyutsu with friends and other cystic fibrosis patients. At age four Lucy went to Scottsdale, Arizona, for her first intensive week of twice daily sessions with Mary. Back home Cynthia continued daily treatments with Lucy. Several months later, there was a hospitalization, but with none of the usual complications. Then, instead of weekly emergency visits, they forgot to go to the doctor for over a year! They were told her recovery was unprecedented.

With twice daily Jin Shin Jyutsu treatments from her mother, by age six, this child who was never going to be able to attend school, didn't miss a day of kindergarten. Though she still required medication and respiratory treatments for CF symptoms, she glowed with vitality and a voluptuous enjoyment of life. At age ten Lucy, a wacky, rambunctious fireball, was no longer able to attend school. For several more years she went to Scottsdale, Arizona for intensive weeks of Jin Shin Jyutsu sessions. By age 14 she had convinced doctors to put her on the list for a lung transplant. Here is an account of Lucy's last week, in her mother's own words.

Age 15. Lucy asks her doctor, "Am I dying?" "You're like a cat, You have nine lives." is the answer. Lucy's awesome vitality and determination have pulled her through so many critical junctures, even seasoned staff assume she'll pull through another. Besides, she still cracks jokes. Still valiantly working to keep her body going, in this last week there's a change: when she speaks of dying there's no fear. Her greatest project, her fear of death, is finished.

Until the moment Lucy's spirit passes from her body no one else is certain what her destiny holds. On her last morning, six weeks before her 16th birthday, she's at the top of her transplant list. Her grandmother and I treat her with opposite fingers and toes: Nana Barbara holding Lucy's fingers while I hold her toes. A little later Lucy's father goes through each finger as I again jumper cable the opposite toes. When we get to the last combination, and I am lovingly "sandwiching" her big toes, a force nearly knocks me off the bed. Struggling to keep conscious, I lie down on the daybed and all other family members leave the room. As I close my eyes I see two nurses roll Lucy over. This is when she leaves her body.

I still wish, often, that things could have played out differently. I miss Lucy, yet the gifts I received through the events of our life together sustain me in immeasurable, mysterious ways. Our path together enables me to share the Art of Jin Shin Jyutsu, the moments of grace when Destiny opens, with others. That duet of #12 and #23; Thy Will and My Will; calls, eludes, mystifies, and transfigures me.

✦✦✦

After nearly 16 years of valiantly living with her illness, Lucy lost her fear of death and her mother discovered a new path in life. I call that transforming. Also transforming was Joni Newcomer's discovery of joy as her father made his transition. He had had Parkinson's for 17 years and was ready to go. During his dying process she continued to hold his #4s. At the moment of his spirit leaving the body, Joni was the only one in the room, holding his #4s and holding his hand. "I've never felt such JOY as I felt when his spirit left the physical body. It was indescribable. It was the greatest gift he ever gave me." This is her story.

My father, Jack, had Parkinson's Disease for 17 years. Parkinson's is a neurological disease. To put it quite simply, it affects the communication between the brain and the rest of the body. The brain says "move your hand" and the body doesn't "hear" it. It is a horrible debilitating disease that, in Jack's case, affected not only the physical body, but also his emotions, his attitude, and literally changed "who he was."

When he was well, he was a sweet, gentle, kind, loving and very generous man. After about ten years of the disease, he was mean, hateful, self-centered, and just horrible to be around. So when I became aware that it was time for Jack to begin the process of making his transition, it was of course, with a bit of sadness, but also with a great sense of relief that he would finally be free of this body that had let him down. His spirit had a tough disease to deal with in this life, and now that he's gone I can see what a great job he did. It was two weeks from the time he started showing signs of dying to the time of his death. So, let me go on to the Jin Shin Jyutsu part of the story.

I've been working with the energy of Jin Shin Jyutsu since 1985, so I'm just a beginner.[1] Eight years ago when Jack made his transition, I was even more of a beginner, but I did know that the Safety Energy Lock #4 is "The Bridge" between Spirit and Matter. I had been praying during this time that Jack's spirit make the best decision for him on whether it was time to go or to stay. Knowing it was his decision, I knew that holding his #4s would not "make him die." It would simply help his spirit connect with the

---

1. There are so many levels of "knowing" Jin Shin Jyutsu, some people consider it a lifetime learning project!

decision. So, as he lay in his bed, mostly unable to move, I gently cradled his #4s and held his hand. I held a few other Safety Energy Locks, but mostly just held his #4s and talked to him to let him know that all was well and that if he wanted to go he could, that it was safe.

I am the only one in my family who believes in a higher power (God, if I may). I knew that as I did Jin Shin Jyutsu on Jack I was connecting with his Higher Self, but I never discussed that with my family. So when it came time for Jack's spirit to finally go, it was a blessing that I was the only one around when it happened. I think he planned it that way.

The morning of Jack's death my two brothers had been with him all the night before, and they had gone home to rest while my mother and I stood vigil. Mom was working on only a couple of hours sleep, so I sat next to him holding his #4s while Mom fell asleep in a chair on the other side of the room. Jack and I were virtually alone and I continued to cradle his head and hold his hand. I felt it was getting close to the time. His breathing was labored, his pulses changed, and I just felt something I'd never felt before. At the moment he quit breathing, as I was still holding him, I "sensed" his spirit leave his body. It is nothing I can quite put into words; it is a feeling that is indescribable. The feeling I had when he made his transition was one of utmost joy, pure bliss and happiness. That is what our spirit truly is: JOY! I believe that I felt the joy of his spirit finally being rid of a body that had failed him and of the joy of finally being with God again. This feeling lasted for a minute or so, because I had to wake my mother to let her know that her beloved husband had died. In all the flurry of the next few minutes, calling my brothers, calling the hospital (we donated Dad's brain to the neurological institute at the KU Medical Center), I continued to feel Jack's presence, but unfortunately it faded quickly.

Luckily, now eight years later, I can bring back that feeling of utter joy and not fear death and know that Jack is spirit and as close as a thought. I truly believe that he waited to die when we were alone, knowing that I was the only one in the family who would appreciate that moment. This was Jack's greatest gift to me.

✁ ✁ ✁

Joni gives us another transformative story of the beautiful and powerful #4s, "The Bridge," and her friend's awakening from a coma.

One of my oldest and dearest friends is an alcoholic. I've known this since we were in junior high school when she talked me into stealing my parents' scotch from the decanters that always sat out on the buffet. Nancy is the one who introduced me to alcohol and drugs way back then. Luckily for me, I am not addicted to these things, but Nancy isn't so lucky. We parted ways after high school, but continued to see each other through the years. Nancy continued to drink and do drugs and hung out with some pretty spooky characters.

Then she met and married Sam and had two adorable children, but she continued to drink heavily. After many unfortunate alcohol related incidents, her husband left her and the court ordered her children be taken from her as well. She pretty much went down hill from there. At one point she was sleeping under a shelf in a laundromat as her "home," the owner feeling sorry for her and letting her stay there. That is where she was when she fell into a coma. A friend brought her to the hospital and the doctors did all they could to keep her alive. She remained in the coma for two weeks. I had driven to Santa Fe from Las Cruces to do Jin Shin Jyutsu on her twice during that time. The second trip up, I was with Nancy and her mother when the doctor pulled us aside and said that we should say our good-byes, as she probably wouldn't make it through the night. I continued to hold her #4s as long as they would allow me to sit in the room, then I said my good-byes and left for home.

Her mother telephoned me the next morning. Nancy had come out of her coma during the night. Now, I can't say for sure that my holding Nancy's #4s and holding some other Safety Energy Locks is the reason she came out of the coma, but I can say for sure that it did at least help. I think her spirit was ready to give life another try, and what a tough decision that was! She was unable to talk or eat for another week or so. When she was finally able to move, she had no muscles in her legs or back to support her, so she had to learn to walk again. She went through physical therapy for months afterwards. The doctors call her their "miracle girl," since, for all intents and purposes, her body had been ready to call it quits.

That was five years ago. I continue to do Jin Shin Jyutsu on Nancy when I see her every few months or so. She has emphysema, still walks poorly, is in constant pain, but the amazing part — the miracle — is that she hasn't wanted a drink or a cigarette since she awoke from the coma. The spirit is strong indeed!

᠅᠅᠅

Life is a mystery. Who can explain the transformation in Nancy that was plain for all to see? Transformations can also be quite subtle. Maybe there were only two people aware of the depth of change in the life of the following lady. Susan Schwartz tells us her story.

Someone working at the Jin Shin Jyutsu office in Scottsdale, Arizona, gave my name to a man looking for a JSJ practitioner in our area. He called and asked me if I would consider working at the home of a woman who had had a stroke. When I said yes, he gave me her address and said he would meet me there for an interview.

It happened to be pouring rain on the appointed day. It took me an hour-and-a-half to get there, and then there were no parking spaces anywhere nearby. By the time I arrived at the address, which turned out to be a rather palatial home, I was drenched to the skin. I rang the doorbell and was ushered, sopping wet, through room after exquisite room, and finally, I was in the presence of a small group of men. They turned out to be the bankers for the woman's estate and they wanted to know what Jin Shin Jyutsu was, and if it could bring the voice back to this woman who had had a stroke. So there I was, a young woman in my late 20s, dripping wet, sitting in this beautiful setting of chandeliers, Oriental rugs, oil paintings, and antique furniture, trying to justify Jin Shin Jyutsu to a group of men who had no idea of anything but money.

Surely it must be obvious to you that I was, to say the least, uncomfortable. That may be putting it mildly. Whatever I said must have given them hope that the woman's voice would return, because they eventually gave me permission to see her twice a week. This 92 year old woman whom I was to meet must have ruled with a very firm hand. Up to now she had absolutely refused any kind of treatment. Evidently she had shut her eyes and refused to cooperate with the physical, massage, and speech therapists who had so far been hired to help her. I had no idea what to expect.

When I arrived the following week for our appointed session, I was met at the door by her companion/nurse, a very handsome young Argentine man. He escorted me upstairs to her bedroom. I was astounded when I saw her. She was gorgeous. She was engulfed in a beautiful gown, her face was fully and beautifully made up, and she wore a Hermes scarf tied in a very unique way around her head. The lavishly curtained and furnished room was filled with enormous bouquets of flowers, which continued to arrive as gifts from around the world the entire time I was with her. I never saw her when she was anything but gorgeous.

When I walked to the bed her eyes were closed and she was obviously very tense. With only the briefest of greetings, I began a gentle Jin Shin Jyutsu session. As I quietly began working on her, I explained that during this process nothing was required of her. She could remain quiet and still, did not need to open her eyes or speak to me. I probably did her #3s with #25 and #11, the #4 flow, #16,17,18,19 flows. While I worked her breathing eased and I could feel the resistance in her body begin to calm. Except for feeling the tension abate, there was no type of communication, no acknowledgement of any sort, except that occasionally she would open her eyes and look at me.

This was the beginning of my visits twice a week. It was a one-and-a-half hour ordeal for me to get to her home. We had an hour Jin Shin Jyutsu session, followed by my one-and-a-half hour ordeal to return to my home. The sessions continued for about six months.

Something about this woman drew me to her. Which surprised me, really, because she was of a world so obviously different from my own. Over time, I began to feel the changes of energy in her body. I could feel her attitudes softening. Although she obviously could be very ornery, she was inviting my presence. She became much more relaxed, softer, gentler. We spoke very rarely. What I was doing didn't require words. Sometimes the Argentine would help, doing Jin Shin Jyutsu from her other side as I told him which places to touch.

Eventually when I arrived, she would sometimes be sitting in a chair, which I saw as an improvement, a willingness to cooperate. The bankers kept talking about "results." That is, was she talking? The result I saw was her responsiveness. When the nurses left the room, and only after the nurses left the room and we were alone, she would pick up my hand and look at me, responding with her eyes. I, too, began to experience a shift in myself as I worked on this woman. I could feel a melting softness in myself as well, my own attitudes changing. I also became softer and gentler. Occasionally I brought my daughter who would sit downstairs and be given cookies. The woman seemed to know this, and be glad.

The bankers continued to be very concerned she was not speaking, thus seeing no progress, where I was seeing huge progress. Everyone was pushing her. I asked if she was tired, and said that it was OK to be tired. She picked up my hand and kissed it. After that she picked up my hand and kissed it every time I arrived and when I was leaving. This was unusual because one arm and side had been disabled by the stroke, and she rarely used the other arm. For instance, she refused to feed herself, but didn't like to be fed by anyone else. Picking up and kissing my hand was a direct action she initiated because it meant so much to her.

She had come to make major efforts to communicate with me. If I would ask, "Does this help you? Does this make you feel more relaxed and calm?" she would blink her eyes at me. When I said, "Jin Shin Jyutsu helps to eliminate all your fears," she would blink back to me. She seemed to need to do what she needed to do, regardless of what others were saying and telling her.

One day I received a phone call from the banker telling me not to come back. It had been decided to discontinue Jin Shin Jyutsu, the only treatment she obviously accepted and appreciated. I felt very sad for the woman. One month later I received in the mail one of her Hermes scarves and a note from the Argentine, thanking me for everything. The woman had died.

This particular case made a profound difference to me. I had been able to feel the quality of change taking place in this woman, and in myself. I could so clearly see the ease and transformation in this woman's life, and in my own. It was the gift Jin Shin Jyutsu gives, a gift both given and received, without words.

༺༺༺

8

Touching:

The Art of Jin Shin Jyutsu

There are 26 specific sites, called Safety Energy Locks
(SELs) on either side of the body along the energy circulation
pathways, or flow patterns. These flows integrate and unify all
of the seemingly disparate parts of the body. The Safety Energy
Locks are like circuit breakers that protect the body when the
flow of life energy is blocked. The point of Jin Shin Jyutsu is
to keep these pathways open by gently touching two of these
"energy locks" at one time, thereby clearing blocked energy.
Mary Burmeister compared the use of the hands to the use
of jumper cables for charging a car battery. There are many
"flows," or sequences of designated places to hold that foster
the healing flow of this life energy. In a Jin Shin Jyutsu class
you are taught many helpful uses of each Safety Energy Lock.

In this chapter we will describe a few very simple ways of
using Jin Shin Jyutsu with critically ill patients, plus several

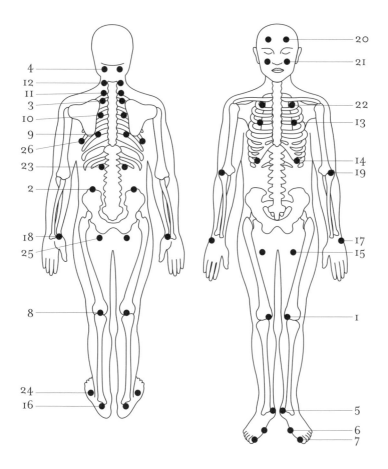

self-help flows for the caregivers. The most important advice I can give you is to find a way to be in a comfortable position as you are giving Jin Shin Jyutsu. If you are straining in a bent-over position, or holding your arm out for too long a time, you will tire and neither you nor the patient will get the full benefit. Pull up a chair to the side of the bed. You may be able to get closer if you turn slightly sideways. Arrange pillows, if necessary, so that your arms are resting in a comfortable position. The more you administer Jin Shin Jyutsu the wiser you will become about which positions work best for you.

Jin Shin Jyutsu consists of touching the body with both hands and maintaining that position for several minutes. The ultimate goal is to feel pulses under each hand that beat simultaneously. Whether you are able to feel these pulses or not, the Jin Shin Jyutsu is still doing its good work.

HOLDING THE #4s

Safety Energy Lock #4 is located at the base of the skull at the occipital ridge, where the neck meets the skull. Remember, all of these SELs are mirrored on either side of the body, so there is a right and a left #4.

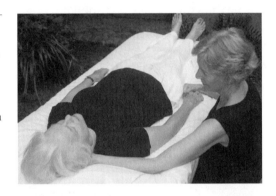

If you are seated on the person's right side, gently slide your left hand under his/her head and "cradle" both #4s. With your right hand hold any finger of his/her right hand.

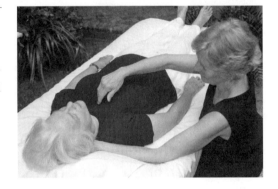

Or with your right hand gently touch the center of the chest area between the breast and the neck. If you are seated on the person's left side, slide your right hand under the #4s and use your left hand to hold his/her left fingers.

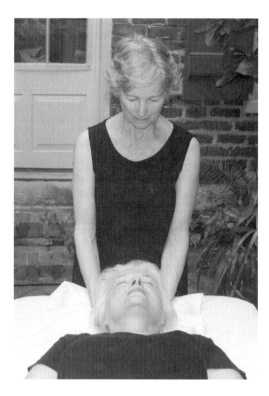

If you cannot reach the #4s from the side of the bed, and it is possible to stand or sit behind the person, simply slide each hand under the back of the head, "cradling" the #4s with both hands.

In Jin Shin Jyutsu the #4s are considered "The Bridge" where Spirit and Matter connect. It is considered the entry and the exit point for the life spirit. Holding the #4s has a calming effect and allows the person, either consciously or unconsciously, to make the decision to go or to stay at that particular time. You may remember in many of the stories there was mention of holding the #4s.

A Hospice Chaplain of three years has told me how she values the holding of the #4s at the time of death, of how calming it is. She thinks the life energy does not necessarily leave the body at the exact time of clinical death. When she is with a dying person and his or her family, she either continues holding the #4s herself or encourages them to do so. On occasion it is possible to feel the life energy, felt as a mild pulsing under the fingertips, lingering there in the #4s even after the person is pronounced dead. I consider this part of "being there" for the dying person. It is difficult if not impossible for us to know exactly when the soul leaves the body, which is one reason we feel inclined to remain quietly beside the dying person even after death is obvious.

HOLDING THE #7s

The big toes are the #7s. Cross your hands, so your right hand is on the right big toe, and left hand is on the left big toe. Holding the #7s has a very calming effect, and it is helpful for nausea. It is also beneficial at the time of transition. If there are two caregivers present, one can hold the # 4s and the other can hold the #7s. If only one person is present, hold the #7s first, then hold the #4s. Remember, these are gentle touches, pressure is not required.

HOLDING THE HAND AND FINGERS

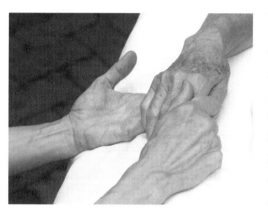

Sitting on the person's right side, simply hold the palm of his/her right hand with the fingers of your left hand. With your right hand hold the thumb and each finger, one at a time.

The thumb and fingers may be held in any order. They may be held gently, pressure is not required. You are welcome to hold them as long as you like. Each may be held for one minute, or for five minutes, or even longer. Of course, you can also do this from the left side. Just reverse, holding the left palm with your right fingers and the thumb and fingers with your left hand. It sounds complicated, but as you do this it feels very natural.

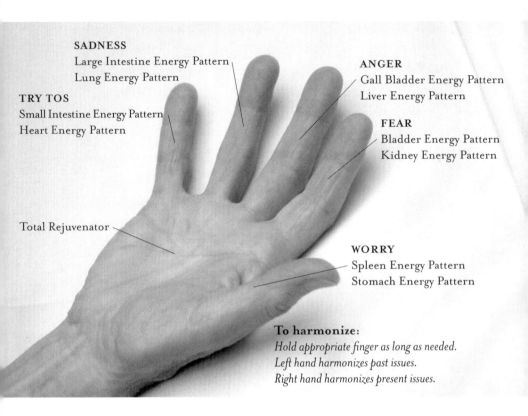

SADNESS
Large Intestine Energy Pattern
Lung Energy Pattern

TRY TOS
Small Intestine Energy Pattern
Heart Energy Pattern

ANGER
Gall Bladder Energy Pattern
Liver Energy Pattern

FEAR
Bladder Energy Pattern
Kidney Energy Pattern

Total Rejuvenator

WORRY
Spleen Energy Pattern
Stomach Energy Pattern

To harmonize:
Hold appropriate finger as long as needed.
Left hand harmonizes past issues.
Right hand harmonizes present issues.

In Jin Shin Jyutsu the thumb and fingers correspond to organ function energy and attitudes, i.e., emotional responses.[1] For instance, in the picture you can notice the ring finger helps lung function, thus breathing, so if the one you are helping has trouble breathing or coughing, spend more time holding the ring finger. Notice the ring finger also helps with sadness (grief). Remember, Jin Shin Jyutsu is about harmonizing

---

1. In Jin Shin Jyutsu the hand and fingers have multiple relationships to the body, including Depths and function energy pathways (meridians). These are explained in much greater detail in a Jin Shin Jyutsu 5-Day Class, or in Alice Burmeister's book, *The Touch of Healing*, available from Amazon.com or www.jsjinc.net.

the body's energy. If someone has either been too angry or frustrated with life, or possibly has been withholding anger, then spend time holding the middle finger. As you look at the picture what is being helped will become clearer to you when you are holding the thumb or any finger. Notice the attitude for the index finger is fear.

The beauty of Jin Shin Jyutsu is that you do not need to "know" what is being helped. You do not need to actually study the chart. You can simply hold the hand and fingers with no knowledge about the organ function energy or attitudes, and the Jin Shin Jyutsu will still be calming, soothing and beneficial to both you and the person receiving.

OPPOSITE FINGERS AND TOES

The Opposite Fingers and Toes flow aids circulation throughout the body. Among other things it is beneficial to those with diabetes or arthritis. This flow helps bloated conditions, swollen legs and feet, and can help ease restless leg syndrome. It also helps to strengthen and harmonize the spine. This is a comforting flow and is particularly good for people who are not used to being touched, because you are only touching fingers and toes. This flow is highly recommended because it helps to harmonize so many functions in the body and is good for overall wellbeing.

Opposite Fingers and Toes can be done with someone sitting/reclining in a chair or lying in a bed. If the person is in a bed, it will be helpful to loosen the covers at the foot of the bed so you can easily reach the feet. Put your chair down toward the lower part of the leg and turn a little sideways. It may help to prop your elbows on the bed. Do whatever it takes for you to be comfortable while you do this.

Sitting on the person's right side, hold his or her right thumb with your left hand, while at the same time you hold his/her left little toe with your right hand. You are holding the thumb of the hand on the same side of the bed you are sitting on, and reaching over to the little toe of the opposite foot. Hold these for several minutes, or until you feel simultaneous pulses in the thumb and little toe.

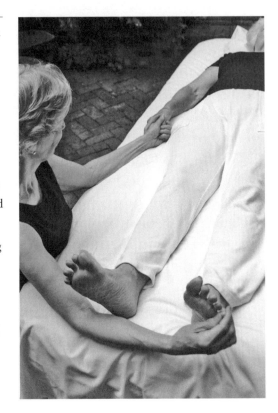

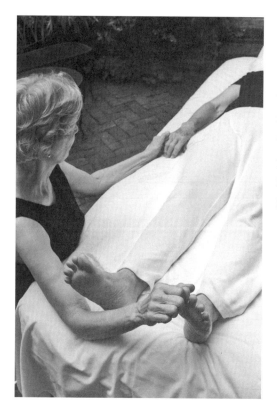

Then move to the index finger and the ring finger and hold them for several minutes. Continue this progression until you arrive at the right little finger and the left big toe.

The same Fingers and Toes flow can be done from the person's left side. From the left side you will hold the person's left thumb with your right hand and his or her right little toe with your left hand, and progress until you hold each finger and toe and arrive at the left little finger and the right big toe.

This is an amazingly restful flow for the patient to receive, and will be restful also for the giver, provided the person giving the Jin Shin Jyutsu has found a comfortable sitting position. Use a pillow under the arm reaching for the opposite foot, if it needs support. When you find yourself getting stiff or uncomfortable, just stop for a while and later begin where you left off. Remember, this is a gentle Art, you can find your own way of using it.

HOLDING THE ANKLES

Standing or sitting at the foot of the bed, with your right fingers touch the inner ankle of the right foot, just under the protruding ankle bone (#5) and place the fingers of your left hand on the outer ankle, just under the outer ankle bone (#16). Maintain this gentle and focused position for four to five minutes, or longer if you have time.

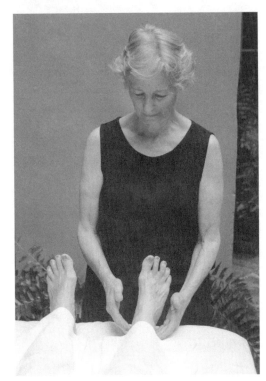

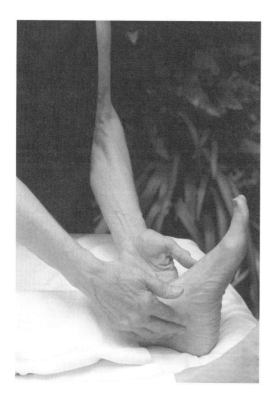

Do the same thing for the left ankle, being sure your RIGHT fingers are on the inner ankle and your left fingers on the outer ankle. When doing this to the left ankle it can be more comfortable for the giver to be standing or sitting just above the ankle on the left side.

Holding the Ankles is particularly helpful for swollen legs and feet, and for easing pain, particularly joint pain. If the legs and feet are severely swollen, do this flow five or six times a day. The Hospice Chaplain I mentioned earlier suggests this flow when a patient is in severe pain and needs morphine. Instead of waiting a long time for the morphine to work, it has been her experience that holding the ankles in this way fosters pain relief within minutes of the morphine being administered.

INSTEP AND LITTLE TOE

Standing or sitting at the foot of the bed, place your right hand on the instep of the right foot (#6) and hold the right little toe with your left hand. Maintain this gentle and focused position for three to five minutes (or less or more as time permits). Move to the left foot and hold the left instep with your left hand and the left little toe with your right hand.

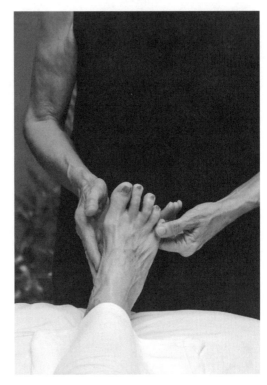

This is another flow that helps swelling, circulation, restless leg, and balance.

PALMING THE CALVES

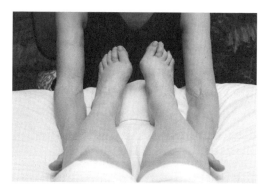

From the foot of the bed slide your open hands under the person's calves, palming the calves. This can be done with your hands straight ahead, i.e., right hand under left calf and left hand under right calf.

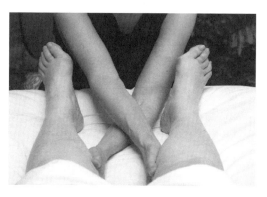

Or you can palm the calves with your arms crossed, your right hand under the right calf and your left hand under the left calf. Try both ways to see which works best for you.

Palming the Calves encourages the passing of gas and aids bowel response. It is also beneficial for skin issues, and it helps to regulate body temperature. Palming the Calves with the arms crossed is preferred, unless this position is uncomfortable for you.

THE BLADDER FLOW

The complete Bladder Function Energy Flow is taught in the JSJ 5-Day Class. A self-help Bladder Flow is found on page 48 of Mary Burmeister's *Self-Help: Book I*. I consider those too complex for the purposes of this book, but because the Bladder Flow is mentioned often in the stories, here are two simple ways to balance the Bladder Flow. This helps many things, including headaches. Also, it is easy to do on yourself as self-help.

BALANCING THE BLADDER FLOW

Simply hold either or both index fingers.

Or, sitting on the left side of the person you are helping, slide your right hand under the neck to the right side of the neck (closer to the back side), midway between the skull and the shoulder blades (SEL # 12). Slide your left hand under the buttocks to the "sit-down" bone (SEL #25). This can also be done from the right side, sliding your left hand under the neck to the left side, and sliding your right hand under the buttocks.

THE SPLEEN FLOW

The Spleen Flow is utilized often in the stories in this book. The complete Spleen Function Energy Flow is taught in the JSJ 5-Day Class. The self-help Spleen Flow is found beginning on page 39 of Mary Burmeister's *Self-Help: Book I*. For this book I describe two simple ways of balancing the Spleen Flow. The Spleen Flow helps energize the body, and benefits both the patient and the caregiver.

BALANCING THE SPLEEN FLOW

Hold either or both thumbs.

Or, sitting on the patient's right side, place your right hand on the inner right ankle (SEL # 5), and slide your left hand under the patient to the coccyx, at the bottom tip of the spine. The hand touching the coccyx can be palm up or palm down, whichever is more comfortable for you. This can be repeated from the left side, putting your left hand on the inner left ankle, and the right hand on the coccyx.

Self-Help

for the Caregiver

Regardless of how much you want to be present and helpful, being there for the person you love can become a physical, mental and emotional drain. The amount of love you feel for the person cannot shield you from exhaustion, and only increases the sadness. It is crucial for you, and for the person you love, to take care of yourself during this time in your life. Jin Shin Jyutsu offers many ways of using Jin Shin Jyutsu as self-help.[2]

This self-help can be done lying down, sitting in a chair, or simply walking around. If you utilize these for yourself, especially with any regularity, you will feel calmer and at the same time, more energized.

I will explain a few simple methods of using Jin Shin Jyutsu that can be helpful during this difficult time in your life.

---

2. Jin Shin Jyutsu Self-Help books and classes can be found on the website: www.jsjinc.net.

HOLDING THE FINGERS

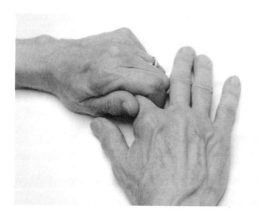

Holding the index finger helps to reduce fear and depression. All ten fingers can regulate over 14,000 bodily functions, allowing us to address a range of issues with fingers alone.

The easiest way to begin is by simply holding your fingers. I understand this sounds ridiculous; but remember, you have nothing to lose by trying it. Hold any finger with the other hand. For instance, begin with the thumb, either thumb. Hold it with the other hand in any way that is comfortable for you. And just sit there holding it. You can close your eyes, keep them open, or be visiting with someone else. Just hold it. After a while — you decide the timing — move on to your index finger. Just hold it. And then move on through the rest of the fingers on that hand.

When you have time, change to the other hand and follow the same procedure. You will be amazed at the calming effect this has. If you are so inclined you can look at the hand in the picture and think about the attitude and organ function energy each finger represents.

THE 36 BREATHS

Counting the exhale followed by an inhale as one, breathe 36 counted breaths. You are breathing out the "bad" and breathing in the "good." Absolutely do not force the breaths. While breathing naturally, the breath will naturally become deeper, though not because you forced it. There are no complications here, no rules about whether you breathe through your mouth, or think particular thoughts, or say a mantra. Just breathe naturally through your nose like you do all day long, and count the breaths up to 36. Jin Shin Jyutsu is so forgiving: if you lose count, just pick a number and keep going. If you fall asleep, that's fine, you needed to sleep. When you wake up just pick a number and continue, or begin again another time.

If you do this with any regularity you will be amazed by the calming and energizing effect. Many people find this more relaxing and energizing than an actual nap. You do not come away from the 36 breaths feeling groggy or fuzzy headed. You feel clear and rested.

THE MAIN CENTRAL FLOW

The Main Central Flow[3] is the primary harmonizing energy flow of your body. The body's energy flows in an oval pattern, going up the back to the top of the head, then down the front to the pubic area, then ascending the back again. When this flow pattern is clear it keeps you in rhythm and harmony with the Source of Life. It recharges you by revitalizing all of the body's other flows.

You can be seated or lying down while you practice this flow on yourself. It is important to be comfortable, so if you are lying down you may want to prop your arms on pillows. It is entirely possible you may fall asleep while doing this flow. You may notice occasional gurgling in your stomach, or you may notice you automatically take a nice, deep breath. All of these are signs your body is relaxing.

---

3. The Main Central Flow is described more fully in Alice Burmeister's book: *The Touch of Healing*, and is taught in Self-Help and JSJ 5-Day Classes.

THE MAIN CENTRAL FLOW

As you assume this position you will understand why you want to prop your arms comfortably. Until the final step, the right hand will remain touching the top of your head while the left hand moves down the front of your body.

1. Place your right fingertips on the center top of your head.
   Place your left fingertips between your eyebrows.

2. Leave the right fingertips on the center top of your head.
   Move your left fingertips to the tip of your nose.

3. Leave the right fingertips on the center top of your head.
   Move your left fingertips to the V at the base of your neck.

4. Leave the right fingertips on the center top of your head.
   Move your left fingertips to the center of the breastbone.

5. Leave the right fingertips on the center top of your head.
   Move your left fingertips to the base of the sternum (the
   pit of your stomach, the soft area where the ribs form a V).

6. Leave the right fingertips on the center top of your head.
   Move the left fingertips to the top of your pubic bone.

7. Leave the LEFT fingertips on the pubic bone.
   Move the RIGHT hand from the top of the head to the
   base of the spine (coccyx). To achieve this position it
   may help to turn slightly on your side. Either the front
   or the back of the hand may be used, whichever is more
   comfortable.

AL'S SELF-HELP JIN SHIN JYUTSU

For heart: each day for five minutes hold the left little finger with the right hand, holding snugly with the right thumb in between the fingers where the little finger connects with the hand.

For headaches: hold for five minutes the inner side of the left or the right ankle, midway between the anklebone and the heel (#5), with the middle finger of the right hand on the inner side of the ankle "matched" by the middle finger of the left hand on the outer side of the ankle (#16). Repeat with the other ankle, retaining the right hand on the inner side of the ankle.

For hay fever: place the fingers of the right hand on the coccyx (the very tip of the tailbone), and place the left hand middle fingers on the inner side of the left ankle for five minutes. Then change and put the fingers of the left hand on the coccyx and the right hand middle fingers on the inner side of the right ankle.

For the immune system: Drape the left hand over the right shoulder and press gently where the middle finger falls, while making a circle by putting the right thumb on all four fingernails, one at a time, for several minutes each. Repeat on the other side.

And/or: Spread the fingers of both hands widely apart and place them on either side of the midpoint on the top of the skull.

For sore throat: Drape the left hand over the right shoulder and press gently where the middle finger lands, and place the right middle finger on the second rib down from the clavicle on the left side of the body (upper chest). Repeat on the other side.

For nausea: Place the right hand on the inner side of the left or right knee and left hand on the opposite inner knee. Hold these two places at the same time.

For eyes: Hold the base of the middle finger on the same side as the eye with need.

For the stomach: The double thumb hold: simultaneously wrap the fingers of one hand around the thumb of the other hand. This is not difficult, but it may take a minute to figure out. With palms facing down and thumbs facing each other, curl your fingers into a loose fist. Now simply slide the right thumb into the left fist and the left thumb into the right fist. Relax with your hands in your lap.

For anxiety: Hold either index finger with the other hand.

Please remember, the Jin Shin Jyutsu described in this book is not only for critical illness. It is useful for maintaining a healthy balance in all aspects of your life. There are many different ways of using Jin Shin Jyutsu to help you restore and maintain a healthy and vibrant life. Though not described here, they are easily found through classes and Jin Shin Jyutsu books. There are teachers worldwide who are trained to give Jin Shin Jyutsu® Physio-Philosophy 5-Day Classes, Seminars and Self-Help Classes. The website is: www.jsjinc.net

I hope with the stories in this book you have been inspired to use the simple Jin Shin Jyutsu described here, both on someone you care for and on yourself. I hope your life is touched by this awareness. I wish for you every possible good.

BIBLIOGRAPHY

Self-Help Book 1: Getting to Know (Help) Myself, Art of Living
by Mary Burmeister

Self-Help Book 2: Mankind's Safety Energy Locks and Keys
by Mary Burmeister

Self-Help Book 3: Fun with Fingers and Toes
by Mary Burmeister

Fun with Happy Hands (for children)
by Mary Burmeister

*The Touch of Healing: Energizing Body, Mind, and Spirit
with the Art of Jin Shin Jyutsu*
by Alice Burmeister

"What Mary Says…"
(A compilation of quotations used by Mary Burmeister)
by Lynne Pflueger and Michael Wenninger

Jin Shin Jyutsu for Your Animal Companion
by Adele Leas

*Jin Shin Jyutsu: Die Kunst der Selbstheilung
durch Auflegen der Hände*
by Waltraud Riegger-Krause